Table of Contents
LEVEL A

helson

P9-CSW-364

Sequence   P.R.

a   a
i   i
u   o
o   e
e   u

Unit 1

Unit 2

Unit 3

Unit 4

Table of Contents
LEVEL A

Unit 5

Unit 6

Here's what to do! **Rake** begins with the sound of **R**. Color 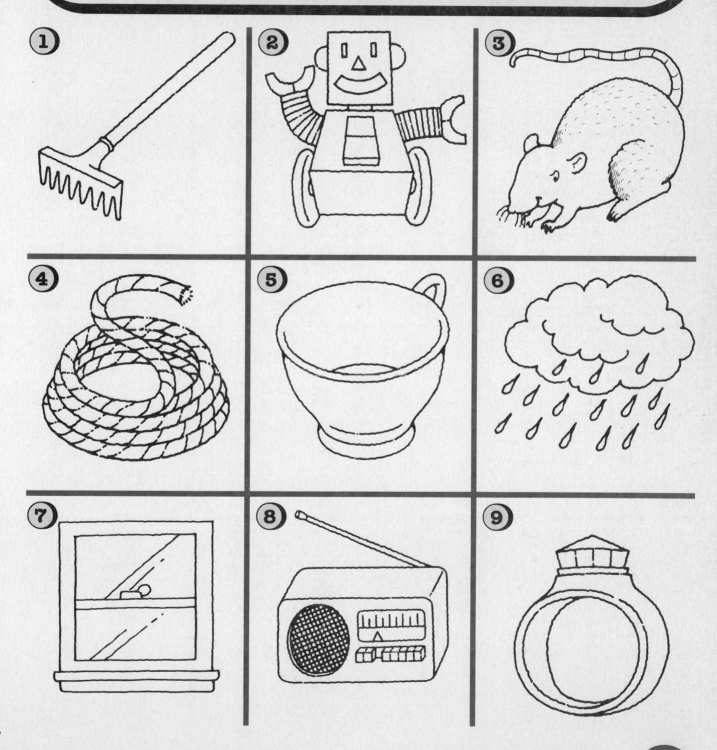 each picture whose name begins with the sound of **R**.

Here's what to do! Say the name of each picture.
If it begins with the sound of **R**, print **Rr** on the line.

1. Rr

2.

3.

4.

5.

6.

7.

8.

9.

10.

11.

12.

Here's what to do! **Pig** begins with the sound of **P**. Color 🖍 each picture whose name begins with the sound of **P**.

Here's what to do! Say the name of each picture.
If it begins with the sound of **P**, print **Pp** on the line.

.

Here's what to do! **Queen** begins with the sound of **Qu**. Say the name of each picture. If it begins with the sound of **Qu**, print **Qu** on the line.

We always stand side by side.

① Qu

②

③

④

⑤

⑥

⑦

⑧

1   V v

2

3

4

5

6

7

8

9

10

11

12

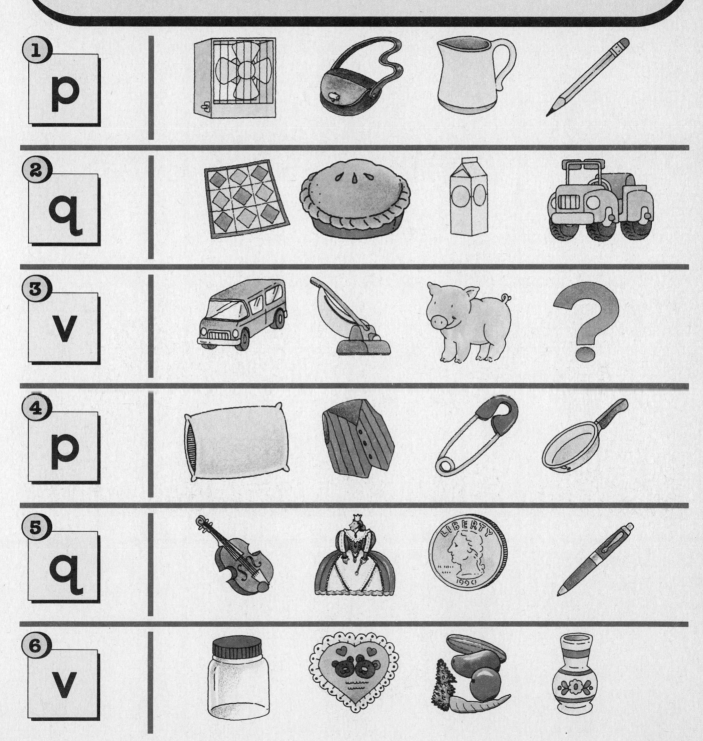

Here's what to do! Look at the letter in each row. Circle each picture whose name begins with the sound of that letter.

1. **p**

2. **q**

3. **v**

4. **p**

5. **q**

6. **v**

Here's what to do!

Say the name of each picture. Print the letter for its beginning sound on the first line. Print the letter for its ending sound on the second line.

LESSON 32: Reviewing consonants W, C, R, P, Q, V

Here's what to do! Color each animal that has partner letters.

Zz go together.

Zz are partner letters.

 ①

Xx zZ Zx Yy

 ②

yY xW Zz xX

Here's what to do! Draw a line from each yo-yo to its partner letter. Color the yo-yo and the partner letter the same.

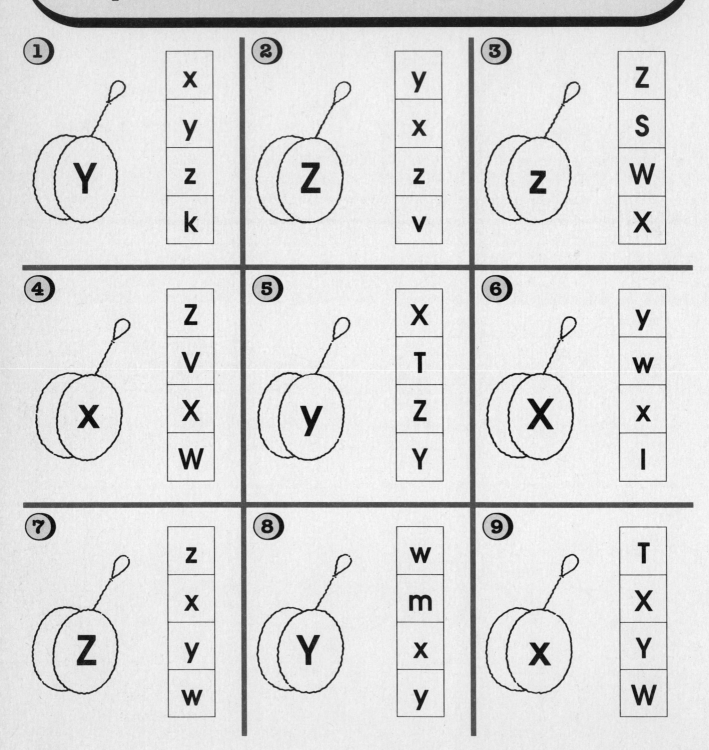

1 Y — x / y / z / k

2 Z — y / x / z / v

3 Z — Z / S / W / X

4 X — Z / V / X / W

5 y — X / T / Z / Y

6 X — y / w / x / I

7 Z — z / x / y / w

8 Y — w / m / x / y

9 X — T / X / Y / W

Here's what to do!
Box ends with the sound of **X**. Color  each picture whose name ends with the sound of **X**.

1.

2.

3.

4.

5. 6

6.

7.

8.

9. WAX

Here's what to do! Say the name of each picture. Circle its beginning letter. Then color each picture whose name begins with the sound of **Y**.

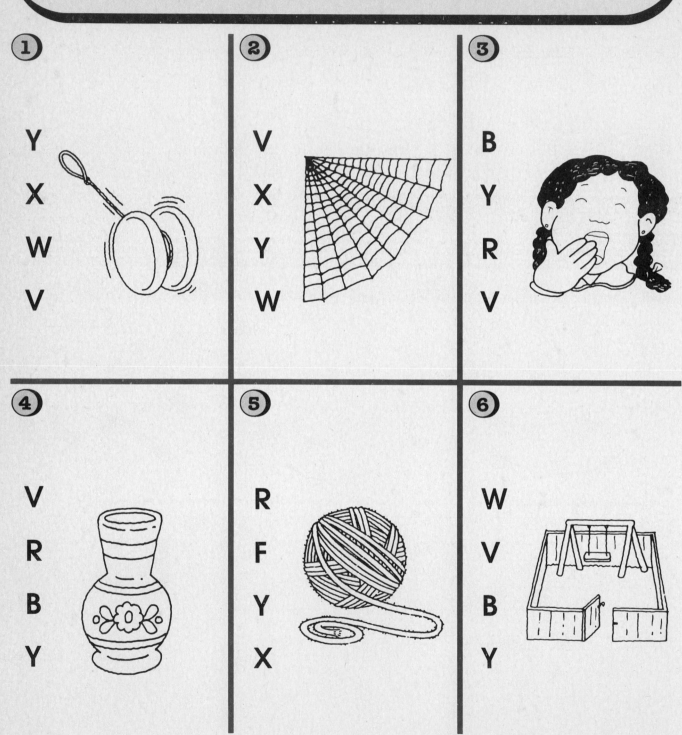

1
Y
X
W
V

2
V
X
Y
W

3
B
Y
R
V

4
V
R
B
Y

5
R
F
Y
X

6
W
V
B
Y

LESSON 34: The sound of Y

Here's what to do! Say the name of each picture. Fill in the bubble beside its beginning letter. Then color each picture whose name begins with the sound of **Z**.

1
○ X
○ Y
○ S
○ Z

2
○ S
○ Z
○ N
○ Y

3
○ Z
○ X
○ S
○ Y

4
○ S
○ Z
○ N
○ Y

5
○ N
○ Z
○ Y
○ S

6
○ X
○ Y
○ S
○ Z

Here's what to do! Say the name of each picture. If the name begins with the sound of the letter in the box, print it on the first line. If it ends with that sound, print it on the second line.

Here's what to do! Say the name of each picture.
Print the letter for its middle sound on the line.

① bab__y

② mo__ey

③ ra__io

④ wa__on

⑤ vio__in

⑥ le__on

⑦ se__en

⑧ spi__er

⑨ dra__on

LESSON 36: Reviewing medial consonants

Here's what to do! Circle the partner letters in each box.

1

A   E

o   a

2

O   o

a   U

3

a   I

e   i

4

e   O

E   u   U

5

e   I

E   a

6

i   u

U   A

7

O   U

a   o

8

I   i

u   E

9

o   U

O   e

10

e   I

i   A

11

A   E

u   a

12

o   A

E   e

Here's what to do! Color the shapes in each box that have partner letters. Use red for one set of partner letters and blue for the other.

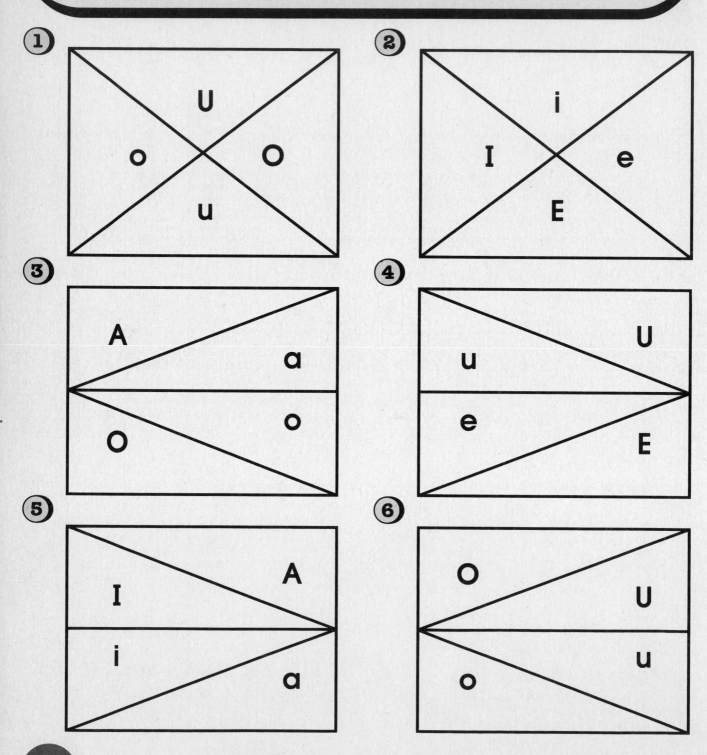

① U o O u

② i I e E

③ A a O o

④ u U e E

⑤ I A i a

⑥ O U o u

LESSON 37: Partner letters Aa, Ii, Uu, Oo, Ee

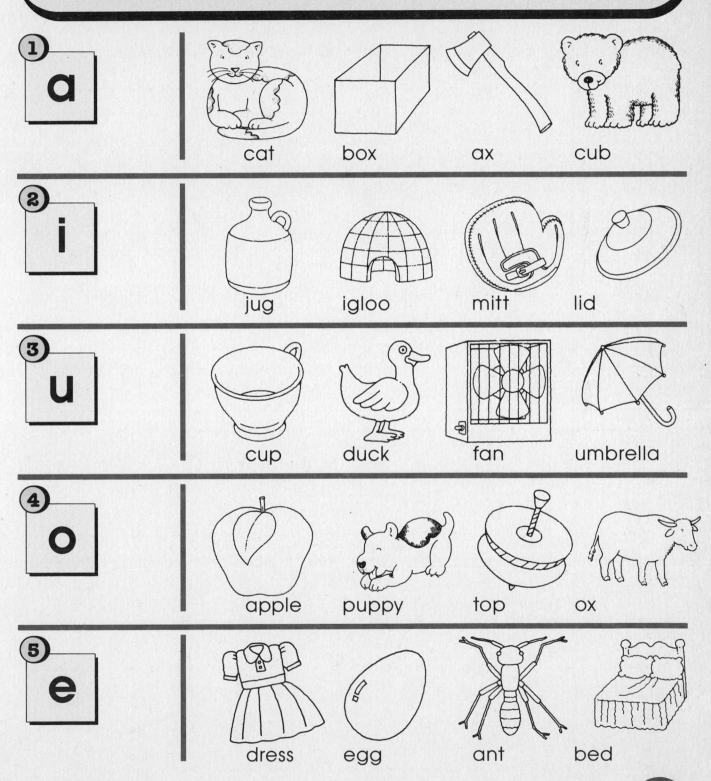

Try this! Look at the letter in each row. Color each picture whose name has that letter.

1 **a**

cat   box   ax   cub

2 **i**

jug   igloo   mitt   lid

3 **u**

cup   duck   fan   umbrella

4 **o**

apple   puppy   top   ox

5 **e**

dress   egg   ant   bed

① a

c a p	a t	l a m p	h a n d
a n d	p l a n t	a p p l e	p a p a

② i

l i p s	g i f t	m i t t	r i n g
q u i l t	m i l l i o n	t i p t o p	t i c k e t

③ u

u p	d u c k	n u t s	s c r u b
s u n n y	h u g s	u n d e r	b u m p

④ o

o f f	m o m	o x	s t o p
p o n d	s o c k	f r o s t	d o c t o r

⑤ e

n e t	h e l p	b e l l	r e s t
e g g	s e v e n	c a m e l	p e n c i l

LESSON 38: Introduction to vowels

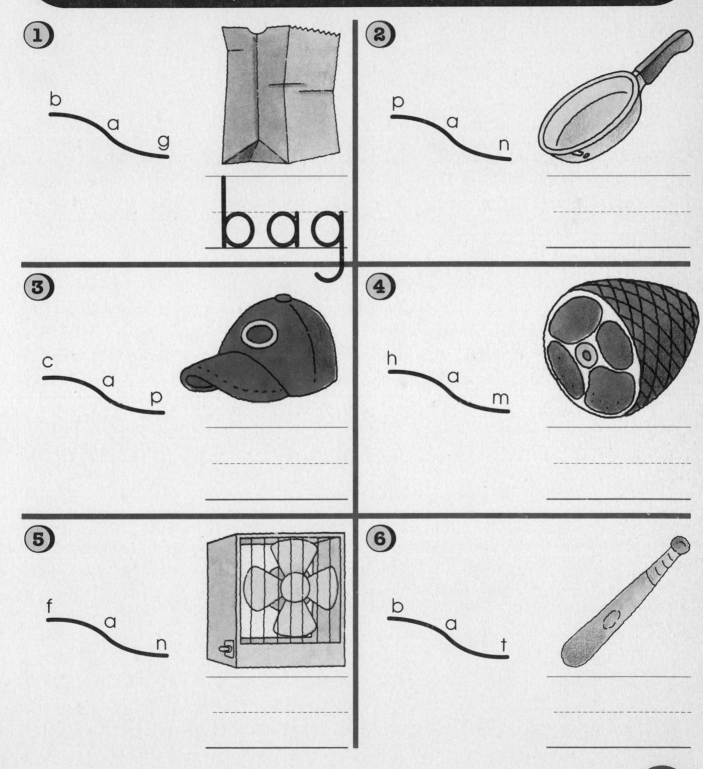

Here's what to do! Say the name of each picture as you slide down the hill. Print it on the line.

1

b
a
g

bag

2

p
a
n

3

c
a
p

4

h
a
m

5

f
a
n

6

b
a
t

79

LESSON 39: Consonant-vowel-consonant blending

Here's what to do! Say the name of each picture as you slide down the hill. Print it on the line.

1

b
u
s

2

p
i
n

3

t
u
b

4

c
u
p

5

p
i
g

6

s
i
x

LESSON 39: Consonant-vowel-consonant blending

Try this! Say the name of each picture as you slide down the hill. Print it on the line.

1. t o p

2. b e d

3. j e t

4. p o t

5. d o g

6. m e n

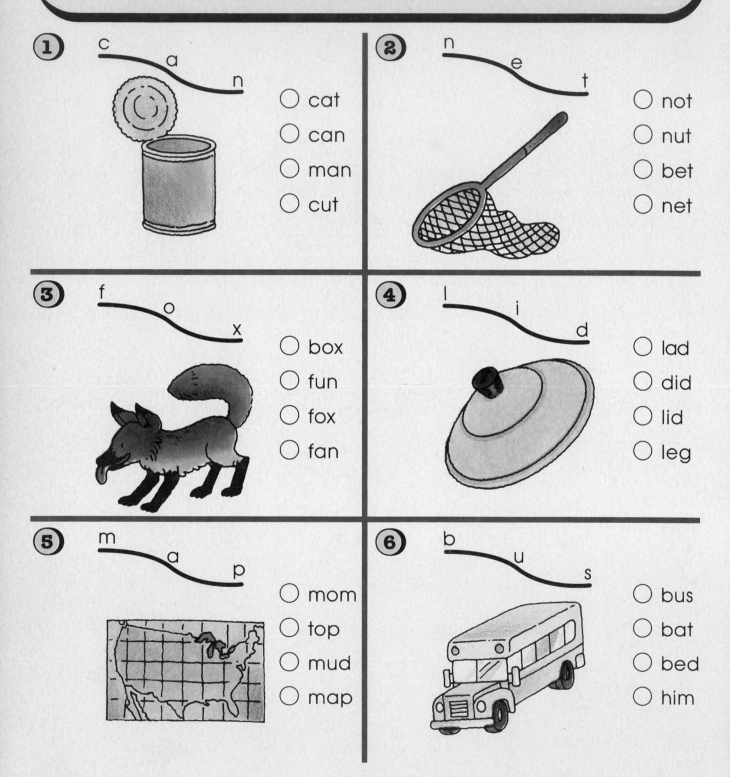

Here's what to do! Say the word as you slide down the hill. Fill in the bubble beside the word.

1 c a n
- ○ cat
- ○ can
- ○ man
- ○ cut

2 n e t
- ○ not
- ○ nut
- ○ bet
- ○ net

3 f o x
- ○ box
- ○ fun
- ○ fox
- ○ fan

4 l i d
- ○ lad
- ○ did
- ○ lid
- ○ leg

5 m a p
- ○ mom
- ○ top
- ○ mud
- ○ map

6 b u s
- ○ bus
- ○ bat
- ○ bed
- ○ him

LESSON 40: Consonant-vowel-consonant blending

Try this! **Ant** has the short sound of **A**. Color each picture whose name has the short sound of **A**.

①

②

③

④

Here's what to do! Say the name of each picture. Circle its name.

1 bat   bad   ban

2 ant   wax   ax

3 nap   can   cat

4 cab   cap   nap

5 man   bag   band

6 tag   rag   tap

7 fat   fan   tan

8 had   hand   land

9 tap   lap   lamp

Here's what to do! Say the name of each picture. Circle its name.

1
tag
bag
wag
bad

2
nab
mat
cab
cat

3
van
mat
man
ran

4
map
man
wag
wax

5
pan
pad
pal
pat

6
cat
rat
ran
rag

7
band
ham
hand
damp

8
ax
an
and
ant

9
camp
ramp
land
lamp

LESSON 42: Short vowel A

Try this! Look at the picture. Circle the word that will finish the sentence. Print it on the line.

1 Max is my _____ .

cat
sat
can

2 He licks my _____ .

land
hand
ham

3 Max sits on my _____ .

pad
rap
lap

4 He plays with my _____ .

sad
dad
bad

5 Max takes a _____ .

nap
cap
cab

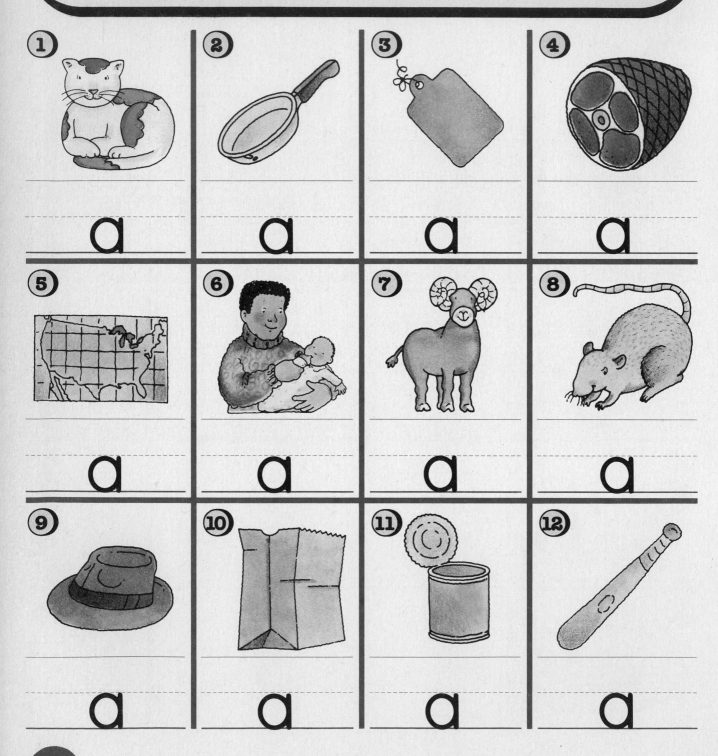

Try this!
Say the name of each picture. Print the letter for its beginning sound. Then print the letter for its ending sound.

1. a

2. a

3. a

4. a

5. a

6. a

7. a

8. a

9. a

10. a

11. a

12. a

LESSON 43: Short vowel A

Here's what to do! Circle the word that will finish the sentence. Print it on the line.

1 It was time to go at ____ .

| lamp |
| land |
| last |

2 Dad and Jan got in the ____ .

| can |
| van |
| cat |

3 Dad got gas and a ____ .

| lap |
| nap |
| map |

4 Jan made a name ____ .

| tag |
| wag |
| tan |

5 She had fun at ____ !

| cap |
| camp |
| cast |

1. fan

2.

3.

4.

5.

6.

7.

8.

9.

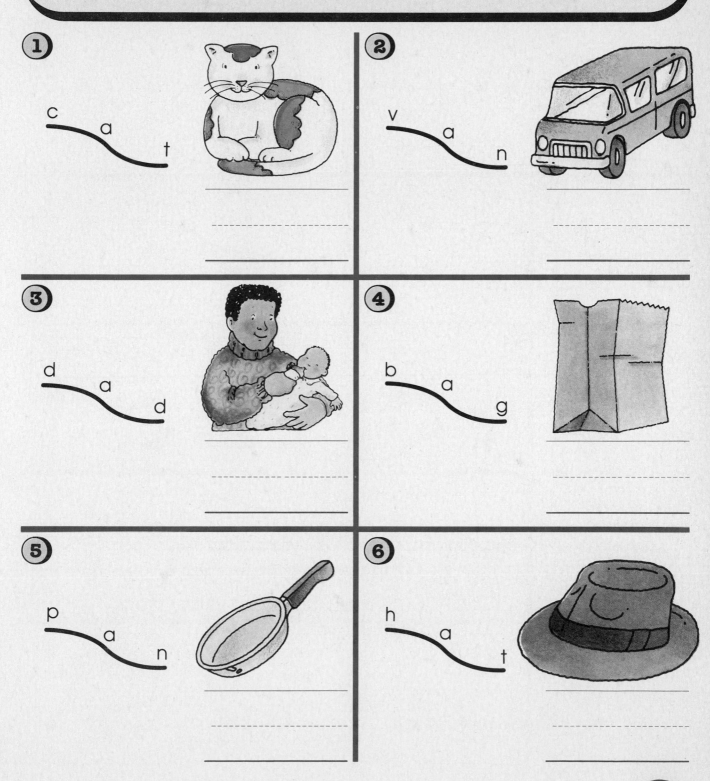

Here's what to do! Say the name of each picture as you slide down the hill. Print it on the line.

1
c
a
t

_____

2
v
a
n

_____

3
d
a
d

_____

4
b
a
g

_____

5
p
a
n

_____

6
h
a
t

_____

① c a p

② r a t

③ f a n

④ b a g

⑤ h a m

92 **LESSON 45: Consonant-vowel-consonant blending**

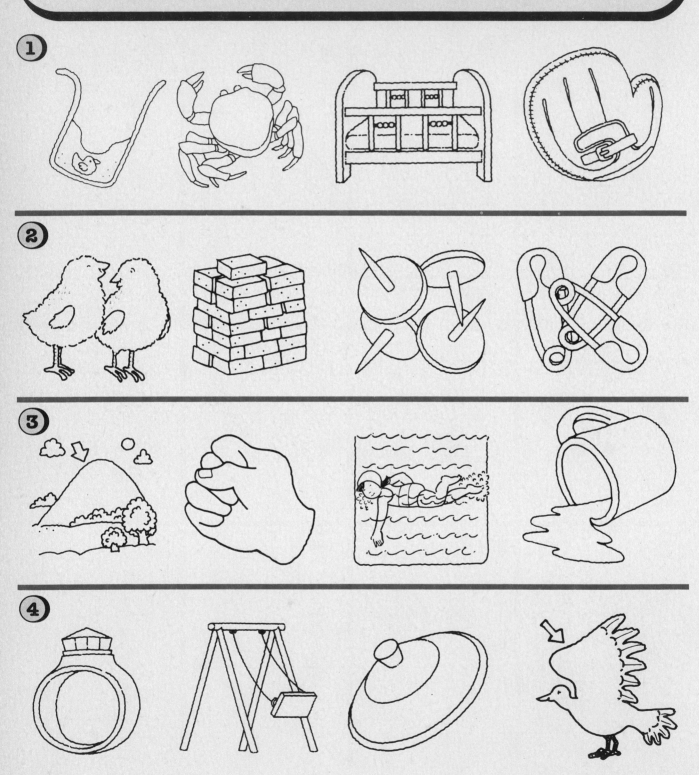

Try this! Circle the name of each picture.

1 dig   big   pig

2 six   sax   mix

3 hid   lid   did

4 bib   bid   bad

5 bin   pin   pan

6 fill   hill   bill

7 mill   mat   mitt

8 rink   sank   sink

9 will   milk   wilt

Try this! Circle the name of each picture.

1

fill
bill
hill
hid

2

pit
pig
gap
pad

3

milk
mill
will
wick

4

silk
sits
sank
sink

5

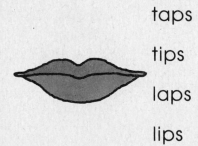

taps
tips
laps
lips

6

quack
quit
quilt
quick

7

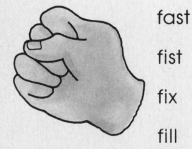

fast
fist
fix
fill

8

lift
gift
fits
wilt

9

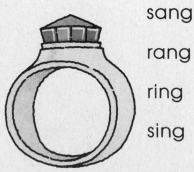

sang
rang
ring
sing

Here's what to do! Look at the picture. Circle the word that will finish the sentence. Print it on the line.

1

I got a _____ .

_____

_____

gap

gift

gills

2

Is it a _____ ?

_____

_____

fill

fan

fish

3

Will it fit in a _____ ?

_____

_____

damp

dig

dish

4

Is it a bit like a _____ ?

_____

_____

milk

mitt

tips

5

Kit

It is a _____ !

_____

_____

fist

hill

kit

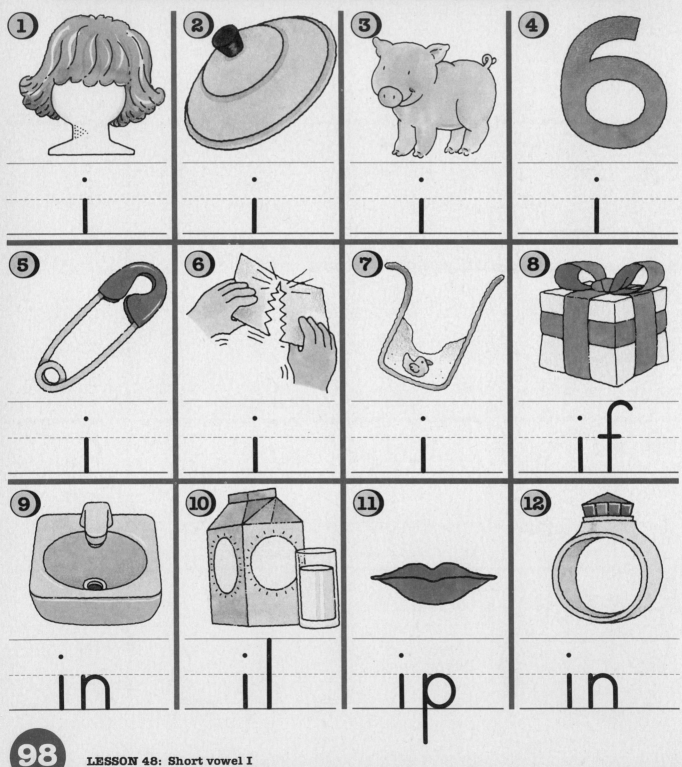

① i

② i

③ i

④ i

⑤ i

⑥ i

⑦ i

⑧ if

⑨ in

⑩ il

⑪ ip

⑫ in

Try this! Circle the word that will finish the sentence. Print it on the line.

1 Jim's bag is _____ .

big
bib
bit

2 He has a bat and mitt in _____ .

if
ill
it

3 His bag has a _____ .

rid
rip
rim

4 Can you fix it for _____ ?

him
hid
hit

5 I will fix it with a _____ .

pig
pit
pin

①

lid

②

③

④

⑤

⑥

⑦

⑧

⑨

Here's what to do! Say the name of each picture as you slide down the hill. Print it on the line.

① p i g

pig

② p a n

③ s i x

6

④ c a p

⑤ r a t

⑥ r i p

LESSON 51: Consonant-vowel-consonant blending

103

Here's what to do! Say the word as you slide down the hill. Color the picture it names.

1 w i g

2 m a p

3 p i n

4 b i b

5 m a n

LESSON 51: Consonant-vowel-consonant blending

1.

2.

3.

4.

5.

6.

7.

8.

9.

10.

11.

12.

Try this! Say the names of the pictures in each row. Color the pictures whose names rhyme.

① ② ③ ④

Try this! Circle the name of each picture.

1. suds   sum   sun

2. gum   mug   gust

3. cut   cap   cup

4. bun   bus   sun

5. bag   bug   big

6. but   tab   tub

7. jug   jab   gum

8. huts   mugs   nuts

9. tuck   duck   luck

Here's what to do! Circle the name of each picture.

①
dump
jump
pump
pup

②
jab
jug
pig
gum

③
fun
ram
run
rim

④
rig
rag
rug
rub

⑤
bin
ban
bud
bun

⑥
duck
buck
luck
tuck

⑦
cat
cub
cuff
cut

⑧
hum
gum
jug
mug

⑨
tank
sunk
run
sun

Try this! Look at the picture. Circle the word that will finish the sentence. Print it on the line.

1 Gus sits on the ____ .

rub
rug
jug

2 He sees the ____ .

bud
bug
bus

3 His pup jumps ____ .

hug
up
cup

4 Gus has to ____ .

rut
fun
run

5 The bus is stuck in the ____ !

mud
mug
hum

LESSON 54: *Short vowel U*   **109**

1. U
2. U
3. U
4. U
5. U
6. U
7. U
8. U
9. U
10. U
11. U
12. U

Here's what to do! Circle the word that will finish the sentence. Print it on the line.

1 It is ____ on the farm.

huff
fuss
fun

2 The pigs dig in the ____ .

must
mud
mug

3 The bugs buzz and ____ .

hump
hut
hum

4 Jen has a ____ .

bun
nuts
sun

5 She feeds it to a ____ .

dug
duck
dump

LESSON 55: Short vowel U

111

Here's what to do! Print the name of each picture on the line.

1.

2.

3.

4.

5.

6.

7.

8.

9.

LESSON 55: Short vowel U

Try this!

Say the name of each picture. Print the missing vowel on the line.

1. b___g
2. b___g
3. t___b
4. s___x
5. p___g
6. r___g
7. c___n
8. r___t
9. w___ng
10. t___ck
11. d___ck
12. m___lk

LESSON 56: Reviewing short vowels A, I, U

Here's what to do! Say the word as you slide down the hill. Color the picture it names.

1. b / u / g

2. c / a / n

3. p / i / n

4. t / u / b

5. r / a / t

LESSON 56: Consonant-vowel-consonant blending

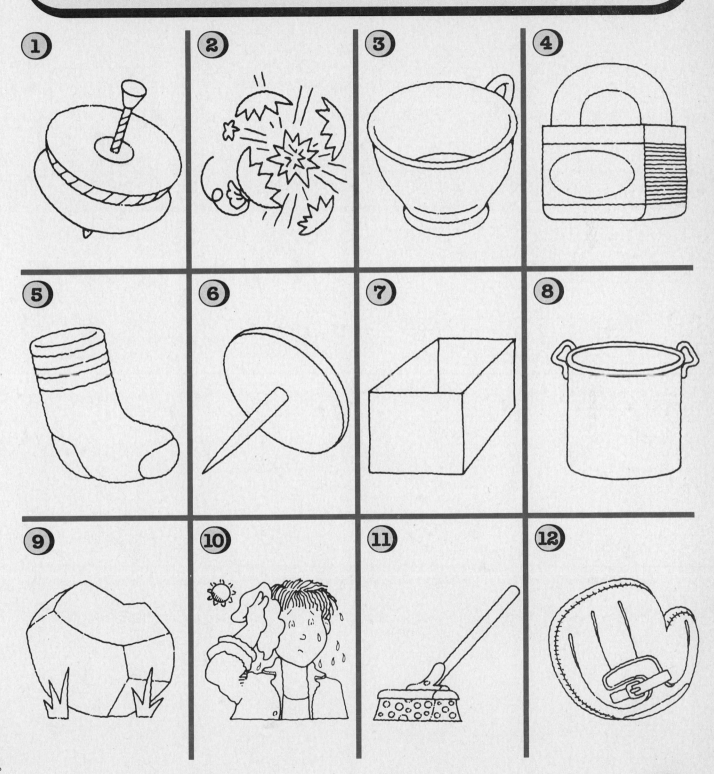

Try this! Say the names of the pictures in each row.
Color the pictures whose names rhyme.

LESSON 57: Short vowel O

1. top   pot   pod

2. box   fox   fog

3. log   dog   lot

4. nap   map   mop

5. tap   tip   top

6. hat   hot   hit

7. dog   dig   dug

8. bat   box   bug

9. fill   dull   doll

LESSON 58: Short vowel O

117

Here's what to do! Circle the name of each picture.

1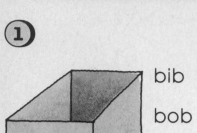
bib
bob
fox
box

2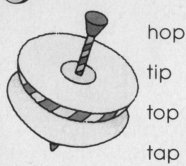
hop
tip
top
tap

3
pop
pup
pad
dog

4
hot
pot
hut
hat

5
ax
ox
six
mix

6
lock
sack
tack
sock

7
rack
rock
tack
tuck

8
mug
map
mop
mad

9
lock
lick
luck
lost

LESSON 58: Short vowel O

Try this! Look at the picture. Circle the word that will finish the sentence. Print it on the line.

1. Bob is ___ .

   _____

   hot
   got
   hop

2. He sits on top of a ___ .

   _____

   ox
   box
   boss

3. He takes off his ___ .

   _____

   rocks
   socks
   locks

4. He sees a big frog in the ___ .

   _____

   pond
   pot
   pod

5. The frog hops up on a ___ .

   _____

   lock
   lost
   log

LESSON 59: Short vowel O

119

Here's what to do! Circle the word that will finish the sentence. Print it on the line.

① Jill likes to _____ .

_____

- - - - - - - - - - - - -

_____

job
jog
jot

② She jogs with her _____ .

_____

- - - - - - - - - - - - -

_____

dot
dock
dog

③ She runs up the hill to the _____ .

_____

- - - - - - - - - - - - -

_____

top
tot
toss

④ She will _____ and rest.

_____

- - - - - - - - - - - - -

_____

soft
stop
sod

⑤ Jill mops _____ her face.

_____

- - - - - - - - - - - - -

_____

on
off
pop

① ② ③

④ ⑤ ⑥

⑦ ⑧ ⑨

Try this! Say the name of each picture. Print the missing vowel on the line.

1. x ___ x
2. ___ x
3. c ___ p
4. c ___ p

5. g ___ m
6. w ___ g
7. p ___ n
8. p ___ n

9. h ___ ll
10. d ___ ll
11. l ___ ck
12. t ___ ck

LESSON 61: Reviewing short vowels A, I, U, O

123

①

A fox is in the box.

A cat is on the rock.

A cat is on the mat.

②

The pig dug in the mud.

The dog is in the tub.

The big dog jumps up.

③

Dot has a map in her hand.

Dot has a mitt and a hat.

Dot has a mop in the hut.

④

Todd picks up his cap.

Todd has milk in his cup.

Todd has a soft pup.

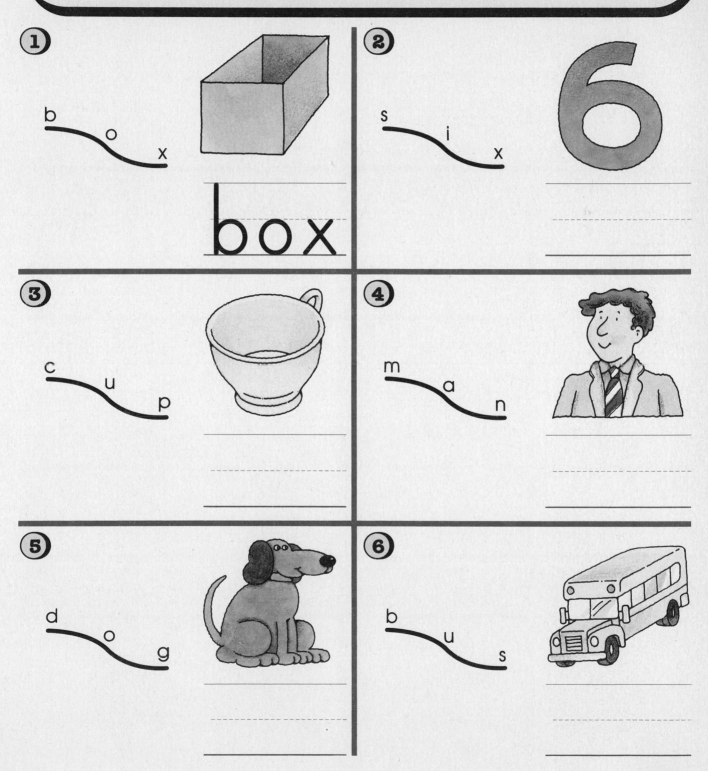

Here's what to do! Say the name of each picture as you slide down the hill. Print it on the line.

1
b
o
x

box

2
s
i
x

3
c
u
p

4
m
a
n

5
d
o
g

6
b
u
s

Try this! Say the word as you slide down the hill. Color the picture it names.

1 l o g

2 b a t

3 c u b

4 f o x

5 p i n

LESSON 62: Consonant-vowel-consonant blending

Try this! Web has the short sound of E. Color each picture whose name has the short sound of E.

(1)

(2)
10

(3)

(4)

(5)

(6)

(7)

(8)

(9)

(10)

(11)

(12)

Try this! Say the names of the pictures in each row.
Color the pictures whose names rhyme.

LESSON 63: Short vowel E

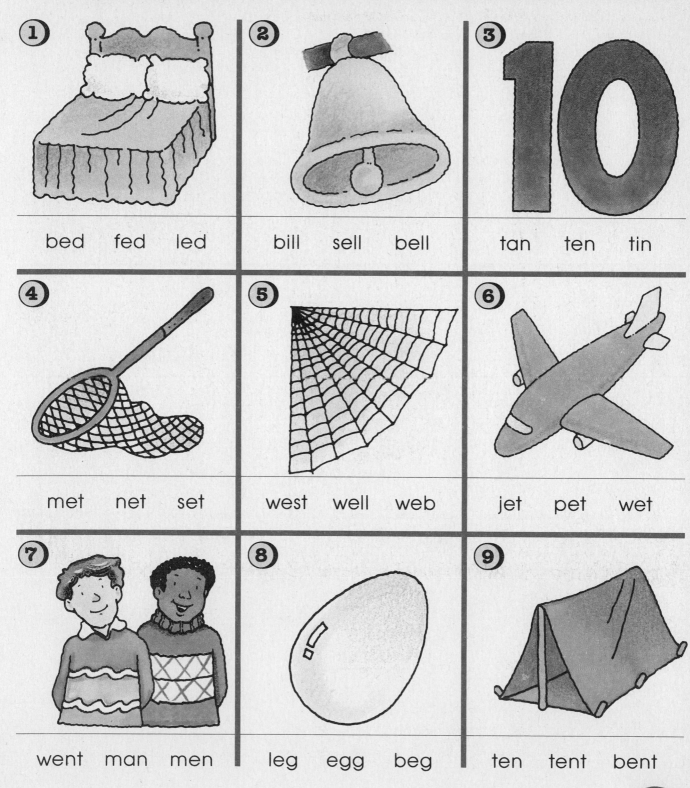

1. bed   fed   led

2. bill   sell   bell

3. tan   ten   tin

4. met   net   set

5. west   well   web

6. jet   pet   wet

7. went   man   men

8. leg   egg   beg

9. ten   tent   bent

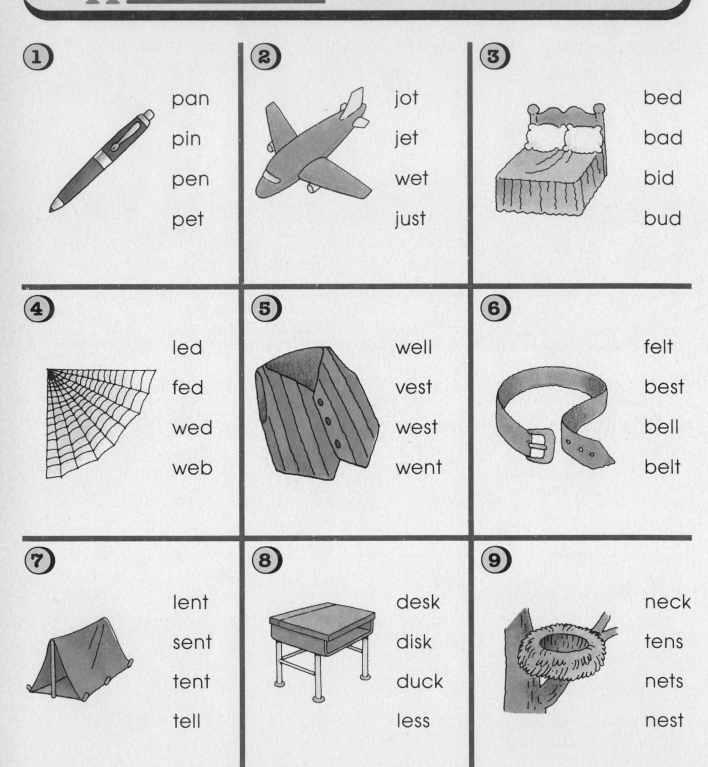

Here's what to do! Circle the name of each picture.

1
pan
pin
pen
pet

2
jot
jet
wet
just

3
bed
bad
bid
bud

4
led
fed
wed
web

5
well
vest
west
went

6
felt
best
bell
belt

7
lent
sent
tent
tell

8
desk
disk
duck
less

9
neck
tens
nets
nest

LESSON 64: Short vowel E

Try this! Look at the picture. Circle the word that will finish the sentence. Print it on the line.

1 Meg sits at the _____ .

dent

desk

den

2 She picks up the _____ .

pen

pet

peg

3 Meg makes a hen in a _____ .

best

nest

west

4 Then she makes a big _____ .

lent

tent

tell

5 Meg gets in _____ to rest.

belt

bell

bed

LESSON 65: Short vowel E

131

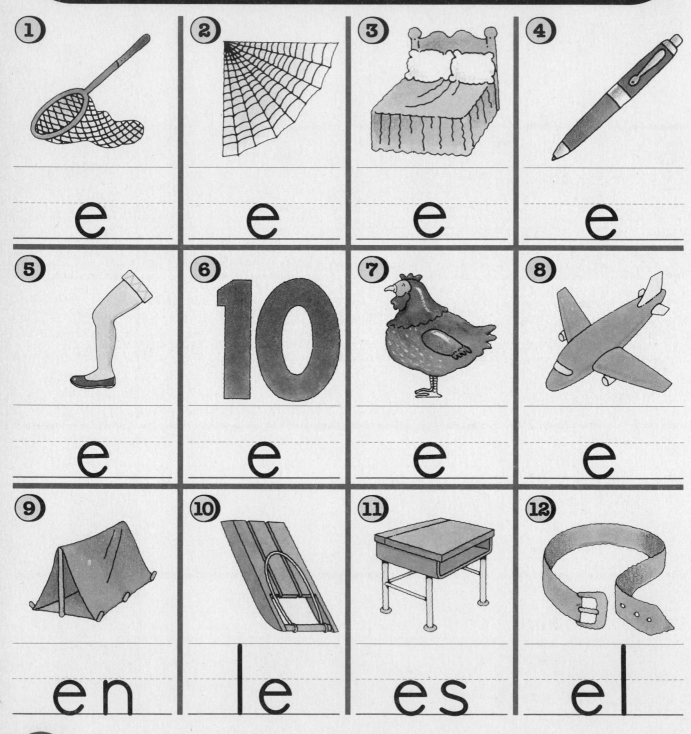

1. e
2. e
3. e
4. e
5. e
6. e
7. e
8. e
9. en
10. le
11. es
12. el

Here's what to do! Circle the word that will finish the sentence. Print it on the line.

1 Ted does not have a ____ .

sell
sled
sent

2 Peg will ____ Ted a sled.

lend
let
leg

3 The sled is as fast as a ____ !

jet
get
met

4 Ted rides on Ben's sled ____ .

nest
net
next

5 He likes Peg's sled the ____ .

bell
best
bent

Here's what to do! Print the name of each picture on the line.

1.

2.

3.

4.

5.

6.

7.

8.

9.

LESSON 66: Short vowel E

Try this! Say the name of each picture as you slide down the hill. Print it on the line.

1 n e t

net

2 m o p

3 s u n

4 w i g

5 c a t

6 p e n

LESSON 67: Consonant-vowel-consonant blending

135

Here's what to do! Say the word as you slide down the hill. Fill in the bubble under the picture it names.

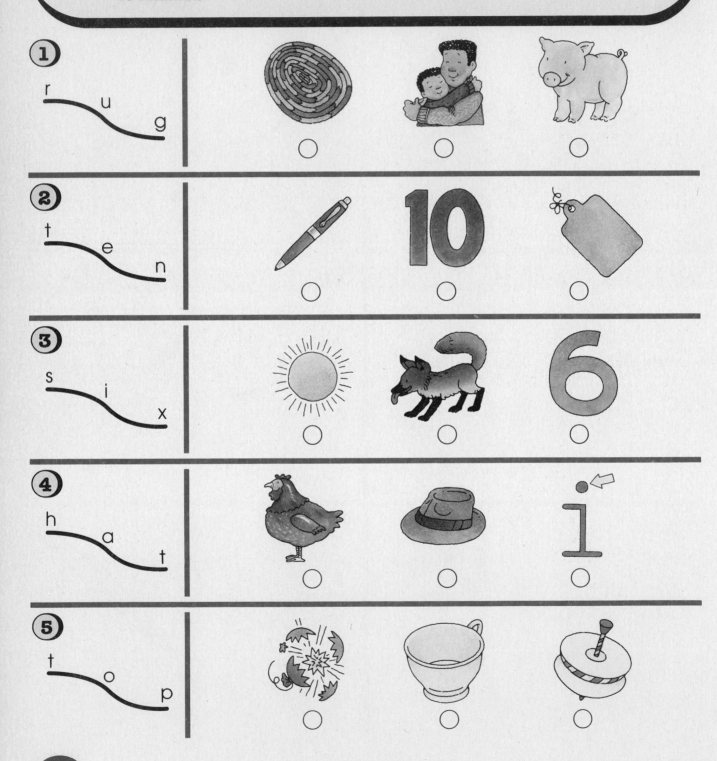

1. r u g

2. t e n

3. s i x

4. h a t

5. t o p

LESSON 67: Consonant-vowel-consonant blending

Here's what to do! Print the name of each picture on the line.

Try this! Fill in the bubble beside the sentence that tells about the picture.

1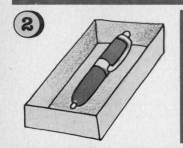

○ Tad has a fan.
○ Todd has fun.

2

○ Jan's pen is in a box.
○ Kim's pin is not in a box.

3

○ The gift is in the bag.
○ The quilt is on the bed.

4

○ The man set up the tent.
○ The men on the bus left.

5

○ Miss Beck rang a bell on the desk.
○ Vic sat and fed a duck in the pond.

Here's what to do! Cake has the long sound of A.
Color each picture whose name has the long sound of A.

Try this! Say the names of the pictures in each circle. Color the parts of the circle that have pictures with long **A** names.

Try this!

Say the names of the pictures in each row. Color the pictures whose names rhyme.

1

2

3

4

Try this! Say the name of each picture. Circle the letters that make the long sound of **A**.

1. rain
2. hay
3. cake
4. mail
5. cave
6. sail
7. pay
8. vase
9. tray
10. game
11. nail
12. lake

1. tape   tail   late

2. sack   lake   rake

3. nail   rail   name

4. case   cap   cape

5. gave   game   pave

6. made   mail   sail

7. gate   tape   date

8. gain   ran   rain

9. cave   save   vase

Try this! Circle the name of each picture.

①

cake
make
cane
take

②

bake
cape
cap
back

③

May
way
hay
hat

④

main
man
ran
rain

⑤

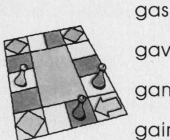

gas
gave
game
gain

⑥

cave
save
case
vase

⑦

day
jay
pay
pal

⑧

tape
tap
pat
bait

⑨

rack
rake
sack
lake

Try this! Say the name of each picture. If the vowel sound is short, color the box with the word **short**. If the vowel sound is long, color the box with the word **long**.

1		2		3		4	
short	long	short	long	short	long	short	long

5		6		7		8	
short	long	short	long	short	long	short	long

9		10		11		12	
short	long	short	long	short	long	short	long

Help Dave, Gail, and Ray find the long **A** words. Circle each one you find.

1

Dave

at	ate	rake	rack
made	safe	tap	tape

2

Gail

rain	ram	wait	cat
sat	sail	main	man

3

Ray

May	man	pay	pat
day	damp	say	way

Here's what to do! Circle the name of each picture.

1	**2**	**3**
rat rate	pane pan	tap tape
4	**5**	**6**
can cane	can cane	hate hat
7	**8**	**9**
cape cap	cape cap	ran rain

1

Kate and Gail go to the _____ .

_____

- - - - - - - - - - - - - - - -

_____

lake
lamp
late

2

They play a _____ .

_____

- - - - - - - - - - - - - - - -

_____

gave
game
gas

3

Gail sits by the _____ .

_____

- - - - - - - - - - - - - - - -

_____

cave
cape
cap

4

She sees a boat with a _____ .

_____

- - - - - - - - - - - - - - - -

_____

tail
sail
mail

5

It makes a big _____ .

_____

- - - - - - - - - - - - - - - -

_____

pave
save
wave

Try this! Say the name of each picture. Print the missing consonants on the line.

1. cape

2. a _ _

3. _ ai _

4. _ a _ e

5. _ a _ e

6. _ a _ e

7. _ a _

8. _ ai _

9. _ a _ e

10. _ ai _

11. _ a _ e

12. _ a _

Try this! Circle the word that will finish the sentence. Print it on the line.

1 The bus was _____ .

lane
late
lake

2 Mom had to _____ .

wait
wade
wake

3 She ran home in the _____ .

rate
rake
rain

4 Mom came in by the _____ .

gain
gate
game

5 She _____ me a big hug.

gave
gain
gate

Here's what to do! Color each balloon that has three rhyming long **A** words.

1. game tame name
2. take tape ape
3. base vase case
4. sail same rail
5. cake rake lake
6. gate date late
7. fade made make
8. bake fake fame
9. nail mail pail
10. rain gain pain

① ② ③

④ ⑤ ⑥

⑦ ⑧ ⑨

Try this! **Kite** has the long sound of **I**. Color each picture whose name has the long sound of **I**.

1

2

3

4

5

6

7

8

9

10

11

12

Try this! Say the names of the pictures in each row. Color the pictures whose names rhyme.

LESSON 76: Long vowel I

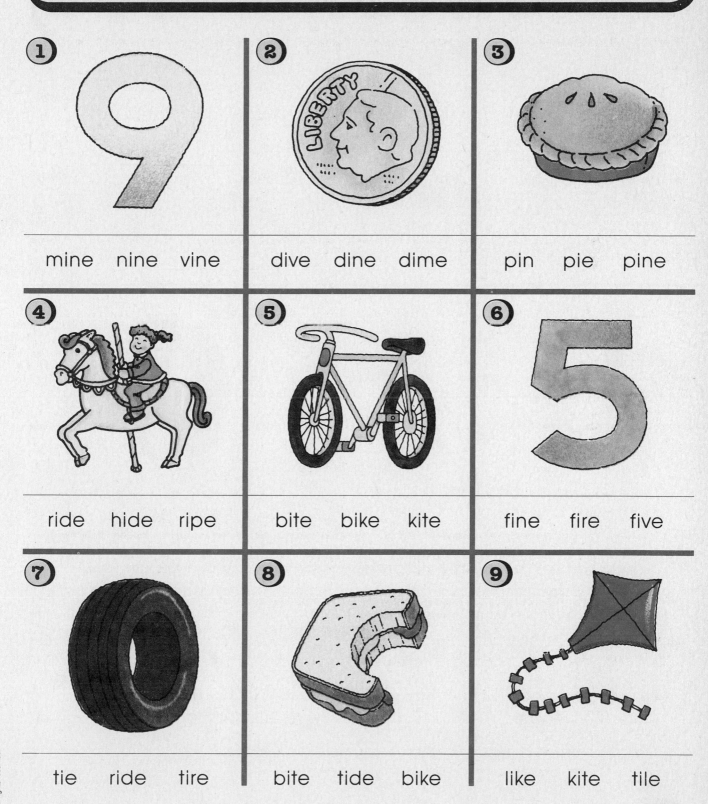

Try this! Circle the name of each picture.

1. mine   nine   vine

2. dive   dine   dime

3. pin   pie   pine

4. ride   hide   ripe

5. bite   bike   kite

6. fine   fire   five

7. tie   ride   tire

8. bite   tide   bike

9. like   kite   tile

LESSON 77: Long vowel I

155

1

tie
pie
lie
die

2

life
file
fire
fine

3

like
line
dine
lane

4

fade
fire
five
dive

5

late
kite
tide
like

6

tire
ride
tame
time

7

fake
bake
like
bike

8

pave
hide
hive
hire

9

dime
dive
vine
dine

Try this! Say the name of each picture. If the vowel sound is short, color the box with the word **short**. If the vowel sound is long, color the box with the word **long**.

1

short	long

2

short	long

3

short	long

4

short	long

5

short	long

6

short	long

7

short	long

8

short	long

9

short	long

10

short	long

11

short	long

12

_____

short	long

Try this! Circle the name of each picture.

1. rid   ride

2. kit   kite

3. pin   pine

4. cap   cape

5. dim   dime

6. rip   ripe

7. lid   lied

8. ran   rain

9. fin   fine

1. Jim has ____ dimes.

   fine
   file
   five

2. He will not get a ____ .

   kite
   bite
   bake

3. Will he get a ____ ?

   lie
   pie
   pile

4. He waits in ____ .

   like
   lied
   line

5. Jim has fun on the ____ !

   rise
   ripe
   ride

LESSON 79: Long vowel I

159

Try this! Say the name of each picture. Print the missing consonants on the line.

1	2	3	4
i e	i	i e	i e

5	6	7	8
i e	i e	i	i e

9	10	11	12
i e	i e	i e	i

_____

- - - - - - - - - - - - - - -

_____

Here's what to do! Circle the word that will finish the sentence. Print it on the line.

1 Mike likes his _____ .

_____

- - - - - - - - - - - - - - -

_____

bite

bike

bake

2 It has a nine on the _____ .

_____

- - - - - - - - - - - - - - -

_____

side

sale

sand

3 It is the same size as _____ .

_____

- - - - - - - - - - - - - - -

_____

miss

mine

mitt

4 Mike will _____ it in the race.

_____

- - - - - - - - - - - - - - -

_____

ride

ripe

rake

5 The race is six _____ long!

_____

- - - - - - - - - - - - - - -

_____

miss

mill

miles

1.

2.

3.

4.

5.

6.

7.

8.

9.

LESSON 80: Long vowel I

Try this! **Tube** has the long sound of **U**. Color each picture whose name has the long sound of **U**.

1
2 June
3
4
5
6
7
8
9

LESSON 81: Long vowel U **163**

Try this! Say the names of the pictures in each row. Color the pictures whose names rhyme.

LESSON 81: Long vowel U

Here's what to do! Circle the name of each picture.

1. rule   mule   rude

2. cup   cube   cub

3. cute   cube   cub

4. tub   tube   tug

5. tune   tube   tub

6. Sue   due   fuss

7. use   sit   suit

8. June   tune   nuts

9. use   sun   suit

LESSON 82: Long vowel U

165

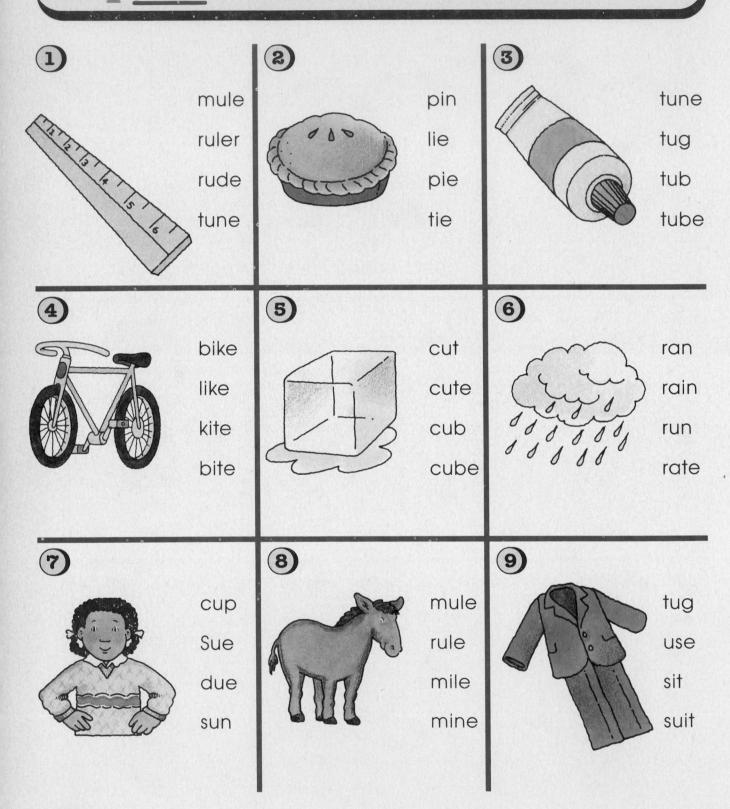

Try this! Circle the name of each picture.

1
mule
ruler
rude
tune

2
pin
lie
pie
tie

3
tune
tug
tub
tube

4
bike
like
kite
bite

5
cut
cute
cub
cube

6
ran
rain
run
rate

7
cup
Sue
due
sun

8
mule
rule
mile
mine

9
tug
use
sit
suit

LESSON 82: Long vowel U

Try this! Say the name of each picture. If the vowel sound is short, color the box with the word **short**. If the vowel sound is long, color the box with the word **long**.

1. | short | long |

2. | short | long |

3. | short | long |

4. | short | long |

5. | short | long |

6. | short | long |

7. | short | long |

8. | short | long |

9. | short | long |

10. | short | long |

11. | short | long |

12. | short | long |

Here's what to do! Color the bubble blue if it has three long **U** words.

1. rude / Sue / use

2. cub / tub / tube

3. line / mine / nine

4. suit / tune / cube

5. mule / rule / tune

6. fire / tire / ride

7. fume / hut / June

8. use / fuse / muse

9. cute / mute / suit

10. pail / sail / tail

Here's what to do! Circle the name of each picture.

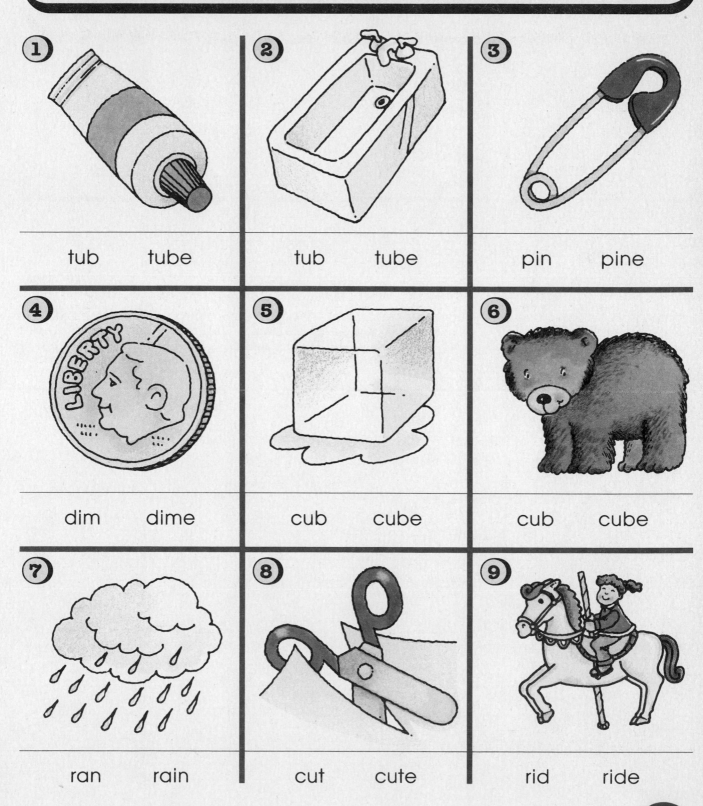

1. tub   tube

2. tub   tube

3. pin   pine

4. dim   dime

5. cub   cube

6. cub   cube

7. ran   rain

8. cut   cute

9. rid   ride

1

Luke has a _____ .

_____

_____

fox

box

ox

2

A box looks like a _____ .

_____

_____

cute

cube

cub

3

Luke has a _____ of glue in it.

_____

_____

tune

tub

tube

4

He will put the _____ in it, too.

_____

_____

ruler

rude

rubs

5

Luke will take it on the _____ .

_____

_____

bug

bun

bus

Try this! Say the name of each picture. Print the missing consonants on the line.

1 u e

2 u

3 u e

4 i e

5 a e

6 u e

7 i e

8 u i

9 a i

10 u

11 u e

12 u e

LESSON 85: Long vowel U

171

Try this! Circle the word that will finish the sentence. Print it on the line.

1 Sue has a _____ .

must
mule
mile

2 Is a mule a _____ pet?

cute
cube
cut

3 Can a mule hum a _____ ?

tub
tug
tune

4 I do not have a _____ .

cute
clue
cuts

5 You can ask _____ .

sun
Sue
suit

Here's what to do! Print the name of each picture on the line.

1. _____

2. _____

3. _____

4. _____

5. _____

6. _____

7. _____

8. _____

9. _____

LESSON 86: Long vowel U

173

Try this! Print the name of each picture on the line. Color each picture whose name has the long sound of **U.**

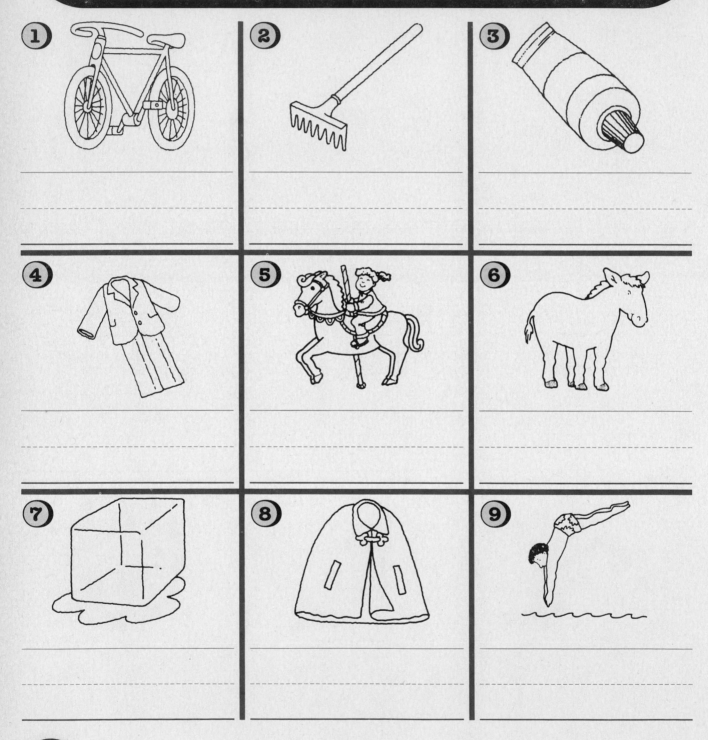

1

2

3

4

5

6

7

8

9

LESSON 86: Reviewing long vowels A, I, U

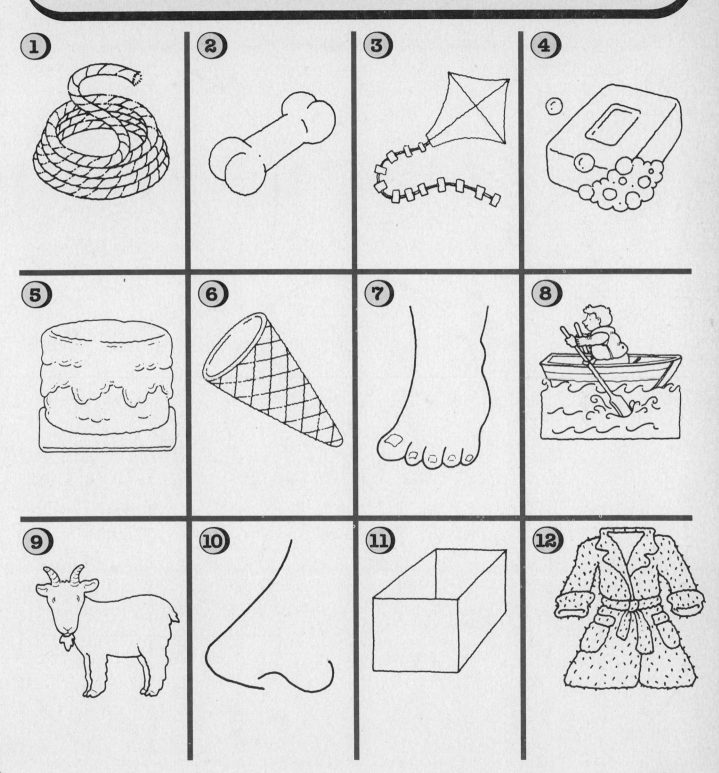

Try this! Say the names of the pictures in each circle. Color the parts of the circle that have pictures with long **O** names.

Here's what to do! Say the names of the pictures in each row. Color the pictures whose names rhyme.

1

2

3

4

1. g o a t
2. b o w
3. n o s e
4. c o n e
5. r o p e
6. b o a t
7. n o t e
8. r o w
9. s o a p
10. h o s e
11. c o a t
12. b o n e

Try this! Say the name of each picture. If the vowel sound is short, color the box with the word **short**. If the vowel sound is long, color the box with the word **long**.

1	2	3	4
short · long	short · long	short · long	short · long

5	6	7	8
short · long	short · long	short · long	short · long

9	10	11	12
short · long	short · long	short · long	short · long

1

bone	cane	loan	moan
can	Joan	tone	run

2

got	boat	coat	note
vote	rate	cute	tote

3

mope	robe	soap	hope
cape	cope	ripe	rap

LESSON 90: Long vowel O

Here's what to do! Circle the name of each picture.

1. cat   coat

2. not   note

3. mop   mope

4. kit   kite

5. bat   boat

6. rob   robe

7. got   goat

8. cub   cube

9. sap   soap

Try this! Look at the picture. Circle the word that will finish the sentence. Print it on the line.

1 A mole hides in a _____ .

hose
hole
hope

2 A fish swims in a _____ .

box
bone
bowl

3 A cat goes up a _____ .

poke
pole
goal

4 A dog begs for a _____ .

bone
robe
boat

5 A fox licks its _____ .

cone
coal
coat

LESSON 91: Long vowel O

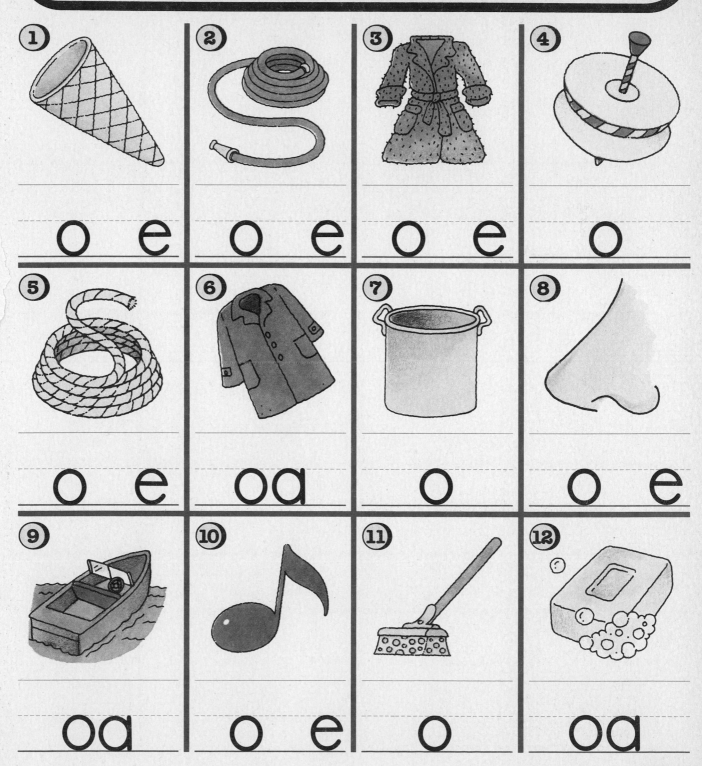

Here's what to do! Say the name of each picture.
Print the missing consonants on the line.

1 _____ o e

2 _____ o e

3 _____ o e

4 _____ o

5 _____ o e

6 _____ o a

7 _____ o

8 _____ o e

9 _____ o a

10 _____ o e

11 _____ o

12 _____ o a

Try this! Circle the word that will finish the sentence. Print it on the line.

1. The shop is up the _____ .

   _____
   _____
   _____

   road
   robe
   role

2. Joan goes in and smells the _____ .

   _____
   _____
   _____

   song
   sole
   soap

3. It gets on her _____ .

   _____
   _____
   _____

   not
   nose
   hope

4. Joan sees a red _____ .

   _____
   _____
   _____

   boss
   bow
   bun

5. She will pay and take it _____ .

   _____
   _____
   _____

   hose
   hole
   home

Here's what to do! Print the name of each picture on the line.

1.

2.

3.

4.

5.

6.

7.

8.

9.

LESSON 93: Long vowel O

187

LESSON 93: Reviewing long vowels A, I, U, O

Here's what to do! **Bee** has the long sound of **E**.
Color each picture whose name has the long sound of **E**.

Try this! Say the names of the pictures in each row.
Color the pictures whose names rhyme.

LESSON 94: Long vowel E

Try this! Circle the name of each picture.

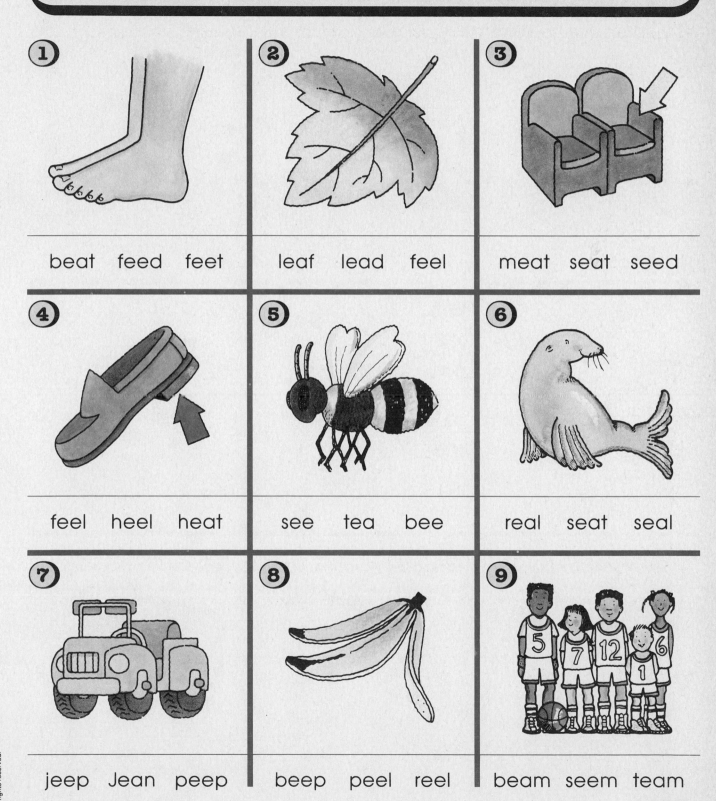

1. beat   feed   **feet**

2. **leaf**   lead   feel

3. meat   **seat**   seed

4. feel   **heel**   heat

5. see   tea   **bee**

6. real   seat   **seal**

7. **jeep**   Jean   peep

8. beep   **peel**   reel

9. beam   seem   **team**

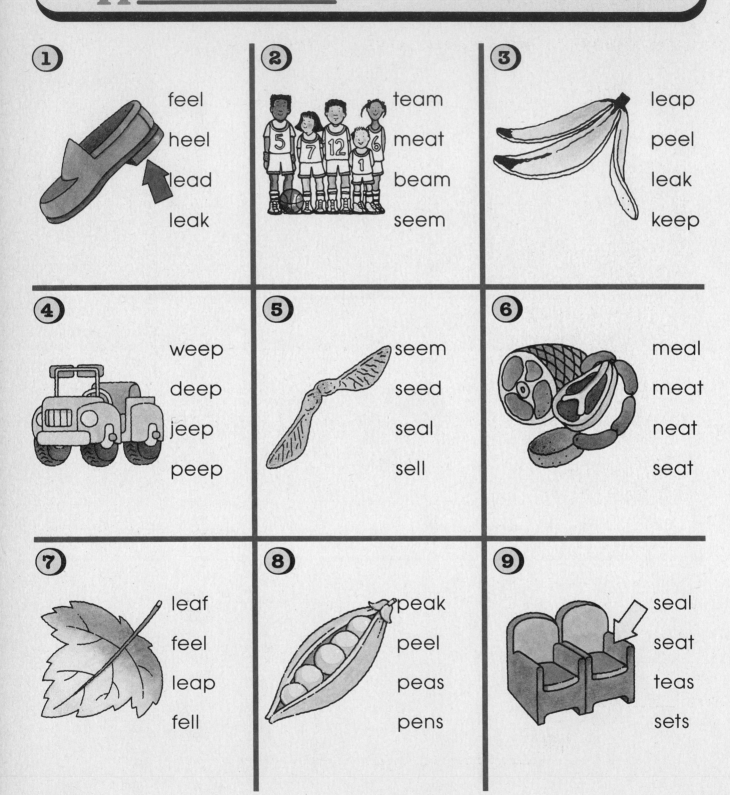

1. feel
   heel
   lead
   leak

2. team
   meat
   beam
   seem

3. leap
   peel
   leak
   keep

4. weep
   deep
   jeep
   peep

5. seem
   seed
   seal
   sell

6. meal
   meat
   neat
   seat

7. leaf
   feel
   leap
   fell

8. peak
   peel
   peas
   pens

9. seal
   seat
   teas
   sets

Try this! Say the name of each picture. If the vowel sound is short, color the box with the word **short**. If the vowel sound is long, color the box with the word **long**.

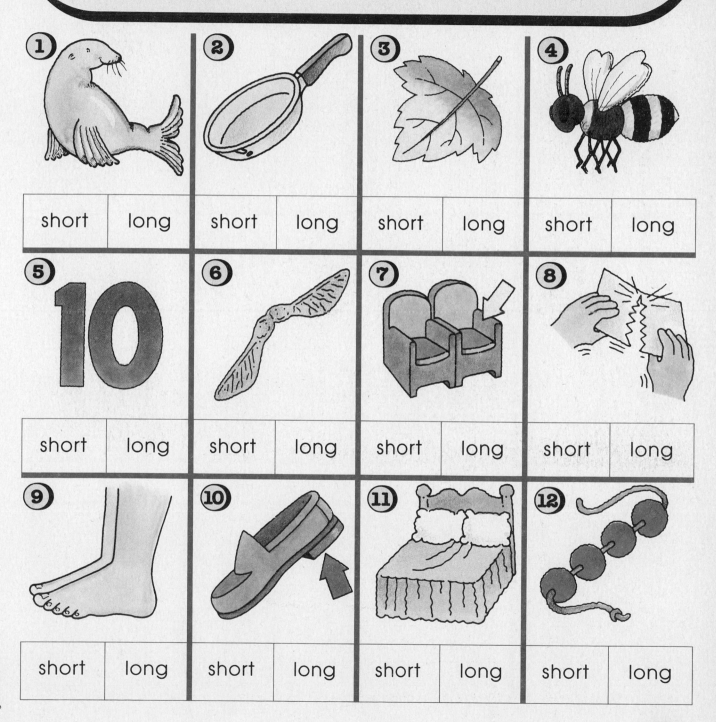

1		2		3		4	
short	long	short	long	short	long	short	long

5		6		7		8	
short	long	short	long	short	long	short	long

9		10		11		12	
short	long	short	long	short	long	short	long

Try this! Say the name of each picture. Circle the words in the boxes that rhyme with the picture's name.

①

me	team	see	met
bean	he	we	fee

②

feel	seal	sell	deep
deal	men	meal	real

③

meat	beat	bet	heat
set	seat	net	neat

LESSON 96: Long vowel E

Here's what to do! Circle the name of each picture.

1. bed   bead

2. met   meat

3. neat   net

4. kite   kit

5. ten   teen

6. set   seat

7. mean   men

8. cube   cub

9. beds   beads

LESSON 97: Long vowel E   195

1 I sit in my ____ .

seal
seed
seat

2 It feels nice to rest my ____ .

feet
feel
feed

3 Dean heats up the ____ .

met
team
meat

4 Mom piles on the ____ .

peak
peas
pens

5 Will you eat a heap of ____ ?

beds
beans
beads

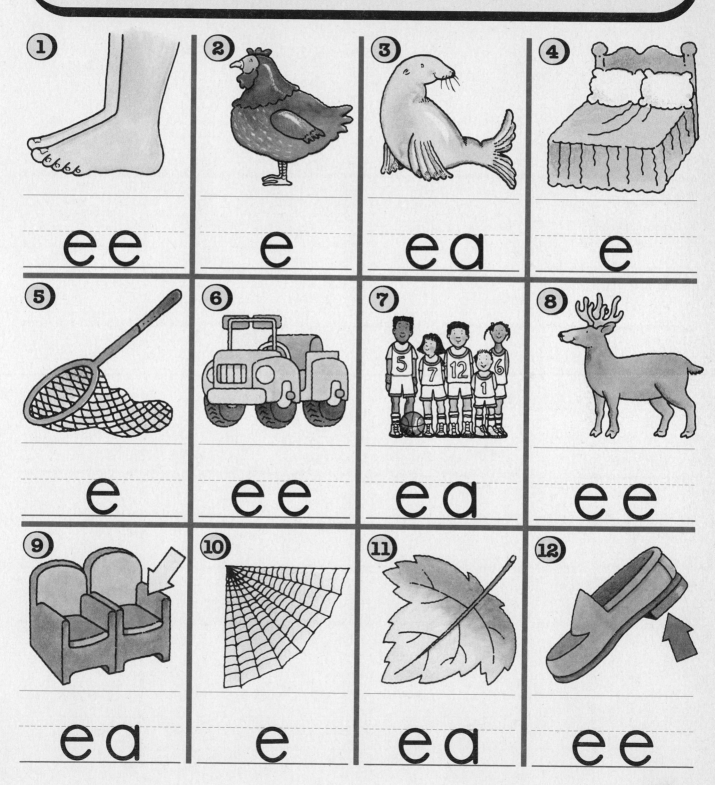

Here's what to do! Say the name of each picture.
Print the missing consonants on the line.

1. e e

2. e

3. e a

4. e

5. e

6. e e

7. e a

8. e e

9. e a

10. e

11. e a

12. e e

LESSON 98: Long vowel E

197

Try this! Circle the word that will finish the sentence. Print it on the line.

1 We rode to Lee's game in the ____ .

_____
- - - - - - - - - - - - - -
_____

jeans

jeep

peep

2 We sat in a row of ____ .

_____
- - - - - - - - - - - - - -
_____

seats

seals

seems

3 The Seals beat the Bees last ____ .

_____
- - - - - - - - - - - - - -
_____

well

week

keep

4 The Bees are in the ____ .

_____
- - - - - - - - - - - - - -
_____

lead

leap

leak

5 Will Lee's ____ win the game?

_____
- - - - - - - - - - - - - -
_____

tent

tame

team

Here's what to do! Print the name of each picture on the line.

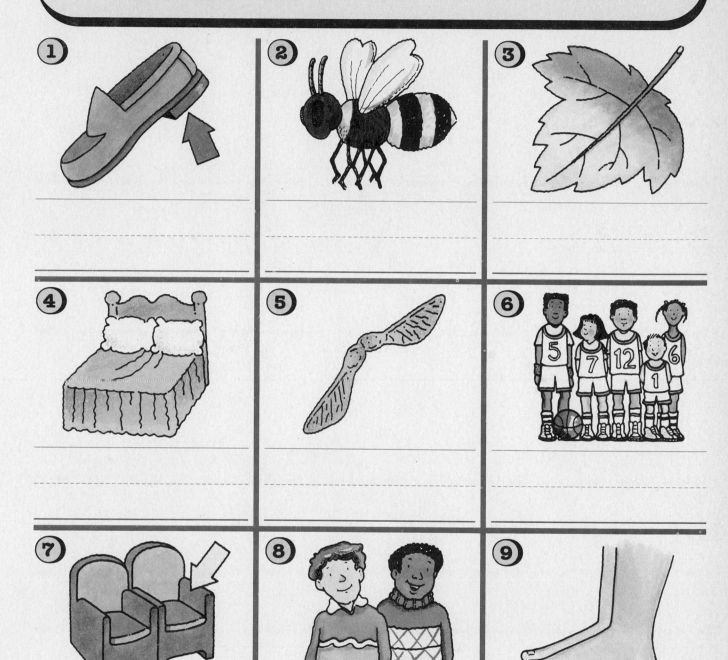

1

2

3

4

5

6

7

8

9

LESSON 99: Long vowel E

199

Try this! Look at the vowel sound. Color the pictures in each row whose names have that vowel sound.

1. Long a

2. Long i

3. Long u

4. Long o

5. Long e

LESSON 99: Reviewing long vowels

Here's what to do! Color the pictures whose names rhyme with the word in each row.

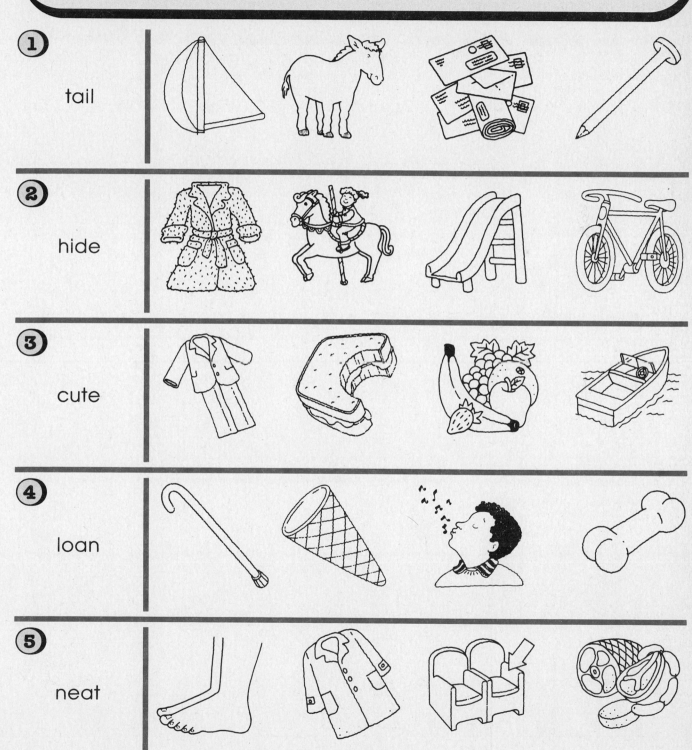

1 tail

2 hide

3 cute

4 loan

5 neat

Try this! Say the name of the picture in each row. Fill in the bubble under the word that has the same long vowel sound as the picture's name.

1

mule   real   mail   nose
○   ○   ○   ○

2

wake   keep   hide   peak
○   ○   ○   ○

3

suit   cape   cone   bead
○   ○   ○   ○

4

ripe   rake   leap   coat
○   ○   ○   ○

5

goat   tube   jeep   game
○   ○   ○   ○

Here's what to do! Say the name of each picture.
Print the missing vowels on the lines.

1. c o a t
2. t r _ _
3. f _ _ t
4. r _ b _
5. t _ b _
6. b _ _
7. d _ m _
8. h _ _
9. l _ f
10. c _ k _
11. s _ t
12. n _ _ l

LESSON 101: Reviewing long vowels

203

Here's what to do! Fill in the bubble beside the name of each picture.

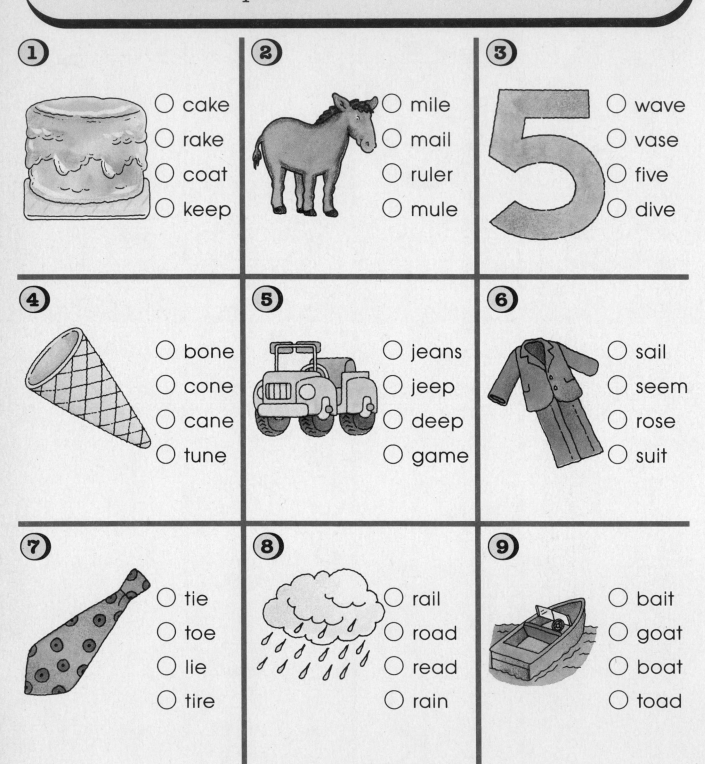

1
- ○ cake
- ○ rake
- ○ coat
- ○ keep

2
- ○ mile
- ○ mail
- ○ ruler
- ○ mule

3
- ○ wave
- ○ vase
- ○ five
- ○ dive

4
- ○ bone
- ○ cone
- ○ cane
- ○ tune

5
- ○ jeans
- ○ jeep
- ○ deep
- ○ game

6
- ○ sail
- ○ seem
- ○ rose
- ○ suit

7
- ○ tie
- ○ toe
- ○ lie
- ○ tire

8
- ○ rail
- ○ road
- ○ read
- ○ rain

9
- ○ bait
- ○ goat
- ○ boat
- ○ toad

LESSON 101: Long vowel test

Try this! Say the name of each picture as you slide down the hill. Print it on the line.

① c u b

cub

② m e a t

③ r a i n

④ p i g

⑤ m o p

⑥ t u b e

Try this! Say the word as you slide down the hill.
Color the picture it names.

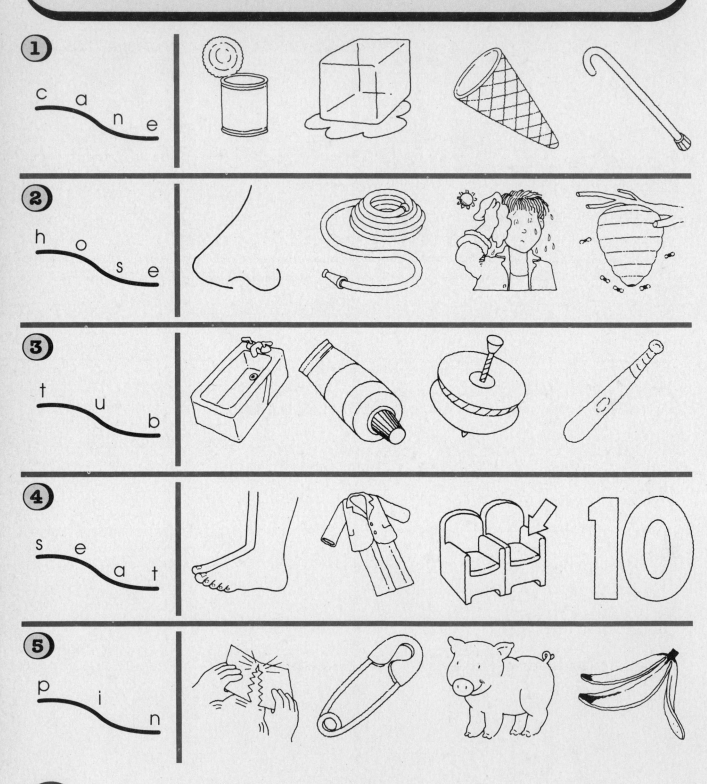

① c a n e

② h o s e

③ t u b

④ s e a t

⑤ p i n

LESSON 102: Reviewing short and long vowels

Try this! Read the first word. Add a vowel to make it a long-vowel word. Then change the vowel in the first word to make a new short-vowel word.

1. at | **ate** | **it**

2. hid | |

3. cut | |

4. hop | |

5. met | |

6. tap | |

7. pin | |

Here's what to do! Circle the word that will finish the sentence. Print it on the line.

1 Sue has a _____ blue kite.

_____
- - - - - - - - - - - -
_____

net

neat

2 The kite does _____ have a tail yet.

_____
- - - - - - - - - - - -
_____

not

note

3 Joe will _____ up rags and make a tail.

_____
- - - - - - - - - - - -
_____

cut

cute

4 I hope it does not _____ .

_____
- - - - - - - - - - - -
_____

ran

rain

5 It is time to sail the _____ .

_____
- - - - - - - - - - - -
_____

kit

kite

Here's what to do! Say the name of the first picture in the row. Color each picture in the row whose name begins with the same blend.

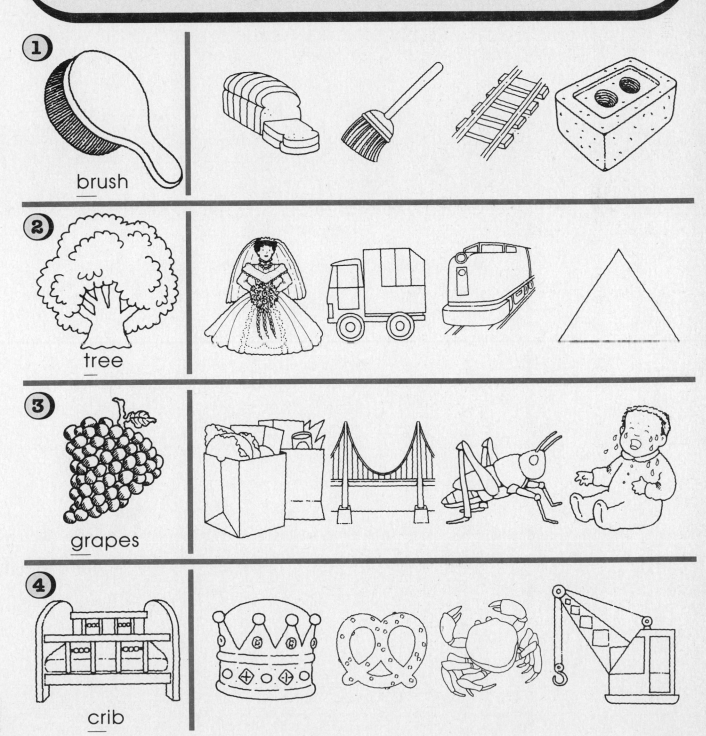

① brush

② tree

③ grapes

④ crib

Say the name of the first picture in the row. Color each picture in the row whose name begins with the same blend.

① prize

② frog

③ dress

④ train

Try this! Circle the name of each picture.

1 free   tree

2 trick   brick

3 prize   cries

4 frog   frame

5 crab   crib

6 drive   dress

7 braid   bride

8 grapes   grass

9 crane   crown

LESSON 105: R blends

211

① ___ab

② ___ain

③ ___ide

④ ___ame

⑤ ___apes

⑥ ___ess

⑦ ___ize

⑧ ___ane

⑨ ___og

Try this! Say the name of the first picture in the row. Circle each picture in the row whose name begins with the same blend.

1. block

2. club

3. flag

4. glass

5. plant

Here's what to do! Circle the name of each picture.

① block flock	② grape plate	③ class glass
④ drag flag	⑤ clue glue	⑥ plug plum
⑦ crack clock	⑧ plant plan	⑨ flat float

LESSON 106: L blends

Try this! Say the name of each picture. Print its beginning blend on the line.

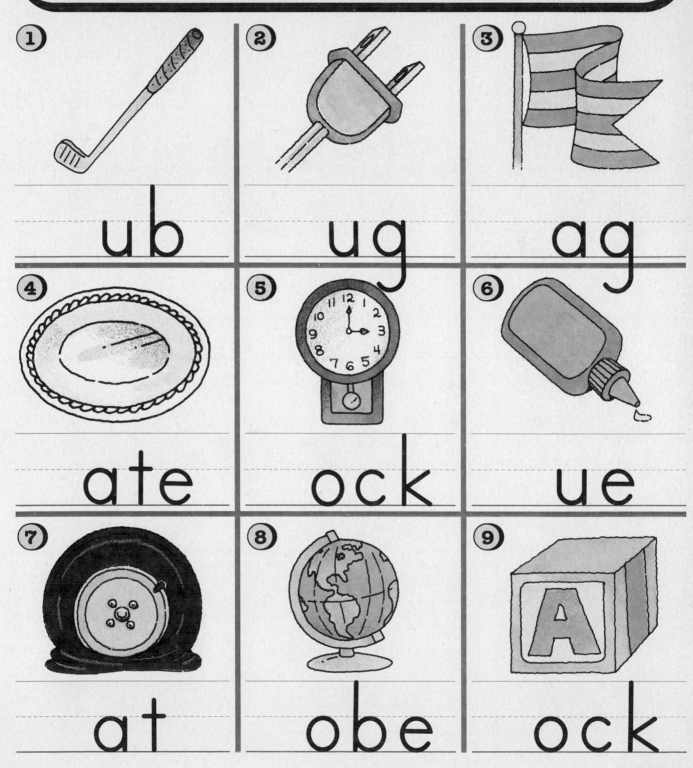

① ___ub

② ___ug

③ ___ag

④ ___ate

⑤ ___ock

⑥ ___ue

⑦ ___at

⑧ ___obe

⑨ ___ock

Look at the picture. Circle the word that will finish the sentence. Print it on the line.

1 Take a peek in my _____ .

clap
class
crib

2 Mr. Glen lets us grow _____ .

plans
plates
plants

3 We can play with clay and _____ .

braids
drives
blocks

4 We find home on the _____ .

globe
glass
grape

5 I am glad my class won a _____ .

plug
prize
prune

LESSON 107: L blends

Here's what to do! Say the name of the first picture in the row. Circle each picture in the row whose name begins with the same blend.

① sled

② spill

③ skate

④ swing

⑤ snail

⑥ stop

1. sled   slide

2. stops   steps

3. spill   spade

4. skunk   spunk

5. spin   swim

6. scrap   scrub

7. sweet   street

8. smoke   spoke

9. square   scare

Try this! Say the name of each picture. Print its beginning blend on the line.

1. __ ate
2. __ ed
3. __ ub
4. __ ing
5. __ ail
6. __ op
7. __ oke
8. __ are
9. __ ill

LESSON 109: S blends 219

Try this!
Look at the picture. Circle the word that will finish the sentence. Print it on the line.

1 Do not cross the _____ .

_____

_____

steps
street
stamp

2 Take turns on the _____ .

_____

_____

slide
sling
slip

3 Do not run near the _____ .

_____

_____

sting
swing
swim

4 Please do not pet the _____ .

_____

_____

snake
spoke
snail

5 Be sure to _____ and read the rules!

_____

_____

spill
stop
star

LESSON 109: S blends

Try this! Say the name of the first picture in the row. Color each picture in the row whose name ends with the same blend.

1. lamp
2. desk
3. sink
4. list
5. swing

221

Here's what to do!
Say the name of each picture. Print its ending blend on the line.

① trunk

② de

③ la

④ ri

⑤ li

⑥ ki

⑦ ne

⑧ si

⑨ ma

Here's what to do! Fill in the bubble beside the word that will finish the sentence. Print it on the line.

1 Brad is the king in the class _____ .

_____

- ○ play
- ○ plan

2 He hems his robe so he will not _____ .

_____

- ○ trap
- ○ trip

3 Brad takes his place on the _____ .

_____

- ○ stage
- ○ string

4 It is time for the play to _____ !

_____

- ○ start
- ○ skate

5 Brad smiles as the kids _____ .

_____

- ○ crib
- ○ clap

LESSON 111: Reviewing blends

223

Try this! Print the name of each picture on the line.

① _____

② _____

③ _____

④ _____

⑤ _____

⑥ _____

⑦ _____

⑧ _____

⑨ _____

LESSON 111: Reviewing blends

Here's what to do! Say the word as you slide down the hill. Color the picture it names.

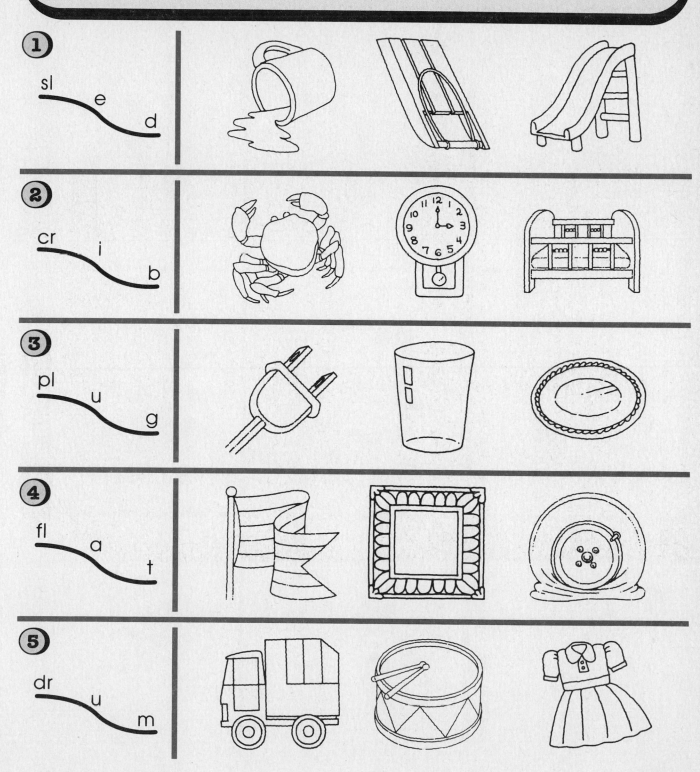

① sl — e — d

② cr — i — b

③ pl — u — g

④ fl — a — t

⑤ dr — u — m

Here's what to do! Fill in the bubble beside the name of each picture.

1
- ○ trip
- ○ prize
- ○ train
- ○ drain

2
- ○ snail
- ○ snake
- ○ skate
- ○ stake

3
- ○ clock
- ○ braid
- ○ track
- ○ block

4
- ○ crab
- ○ grab
- ○ club
- ○ crib

5
- ○ flag
- ○ frame
- ○ flat
- ○ frog

6
- ○ green
- ○ dress
- ○ dream
- ○ drive

7
- ○ swim
- ○ smoke
- ○ swing
- ○ sweet

8
- ○ clap
- ○ plant
- ○ globe
- ○ plate

9
- ○ stamp
- ○ steps
- ○ stop
- ○ spill

LESSON 112: Consonant blend test

Try this! Say the name of the picture. Circle the words in the boxes with the same sound of **Y** as the picture's name. Color the picture whose name has the consonant sound of **Y**.

1

by	lazy	yellow	dry
yet	my	sky	yoke

2

yes	fry	you	yard
funny	yell	puppy	sly

3

fly	candy	yams	lady
penny	pry	fairy	baby

Try this! Circle the name of each picture.

1. puppy   buggy

2. fry   fly

3. lady   baby

4. funny   penny

5. pony   penny

6. cry   try

7. spy   sky

8. fifty   twenty

9. sly   fry

Here's what to do! Look at the picture. Circle the word that will finish the sentence. Print it on the line.

① Wendy can not ride a _____ .

bony
pony
penny

② She is too small to feed a _____ .

puffy
poppy
puppy

③ She can't draw the _____ .

sky
sly
spy

④ I feel sad if she starts to _____ .

my
cry
try

⑤ Wendy is just a tiny _____ .

bunny
baby
buggy

Try this! Say the name of each picture. Print the ending you see in the corner of the box to finish its name.

① ed — spilled

② ed — melt

③ ing — eat

④ ing — rain

⑤ ed — peel

⑥ ing — fish

⑦ ed — jump

⑧ ed — mail

⑨ ing — cook

1

passed	stamped	fixed	played
mixed	rocked	bumped	rained

jumped

2

going	telling	sailing	mixing
asking	waiting	resting	boating

reading

3

waited	seated	heated	landed
needed	loaded	floated	ended

melted

_____

- - - - - - - - - - - - - - - - -

_____

Here's what to do! Circle the word that will finish the sentence. Print it on the line.

1 We were _____ to eat.

waiting
waited

2 Dad was _____ the ham.

cooking
cooked

3 Mom _____ us to help, too.

asking
asked

4 Sandy _____ the fruit.

peeling
peeled

5 I _____ the eggs and toast.

fixing
fixed

1 Dad was _____ fishing.

go

going

2 I _____ him to take me to Mary's home.

ask

asked

3 Mary and I _____ on her swing set.

played

playing

4 Just then we _____ to get wet.

started

starting

5 It was _____ cats and dogs!

rain

raining

Try this!

Thumb begins with the sound of **th**. Color each picture whose name begins with the sound of **th**.

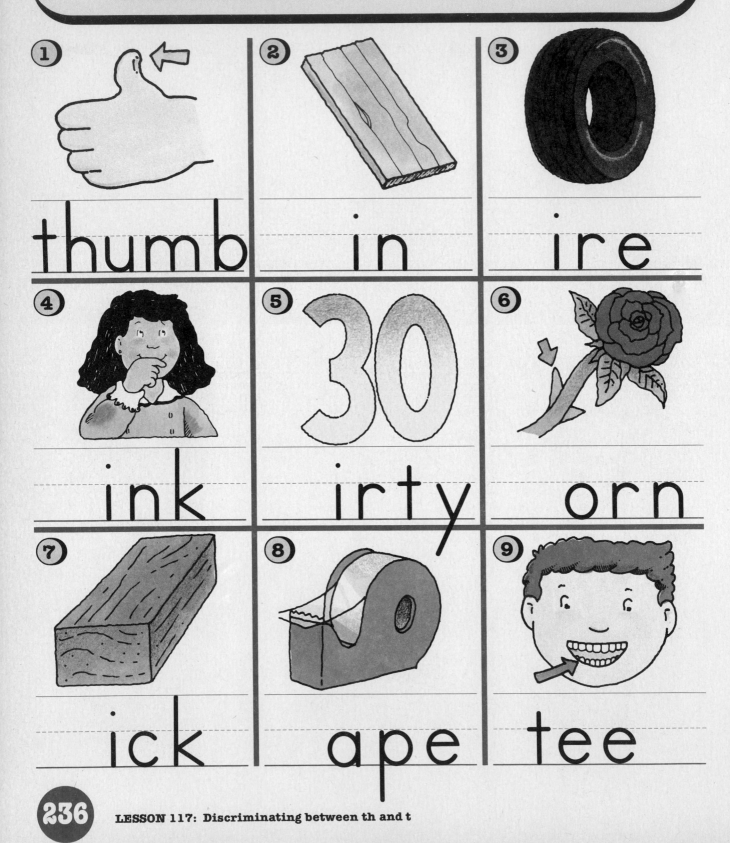

① thumb

② in

③ ire

④ ink

⑤ irty

⑥ orn

⑦ ick

⑧ ape

⑨ tee

Here's what to do! **Wheel** begins with the sound of **wh**. Color each picture whose name begins with the sound of **wh**.

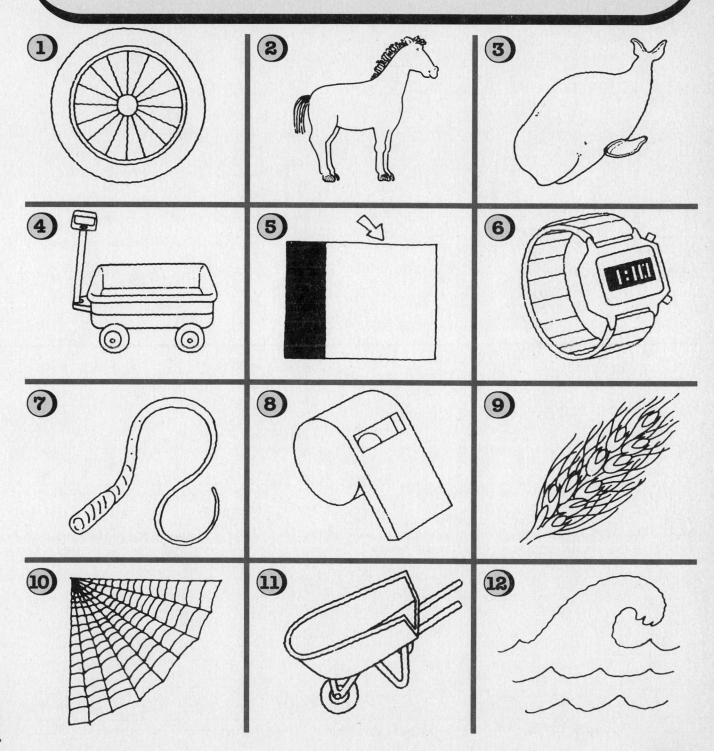

1. ___eel

2. ___umb

3. ___ip

4. ___orn

5. ___eat

6. ___ink

7. ___ale

8. ___in

9. ___ite

Try this! **Sheep** begins with the sound of **sh**. Color each picture whose name begins with the sound of **sh**.

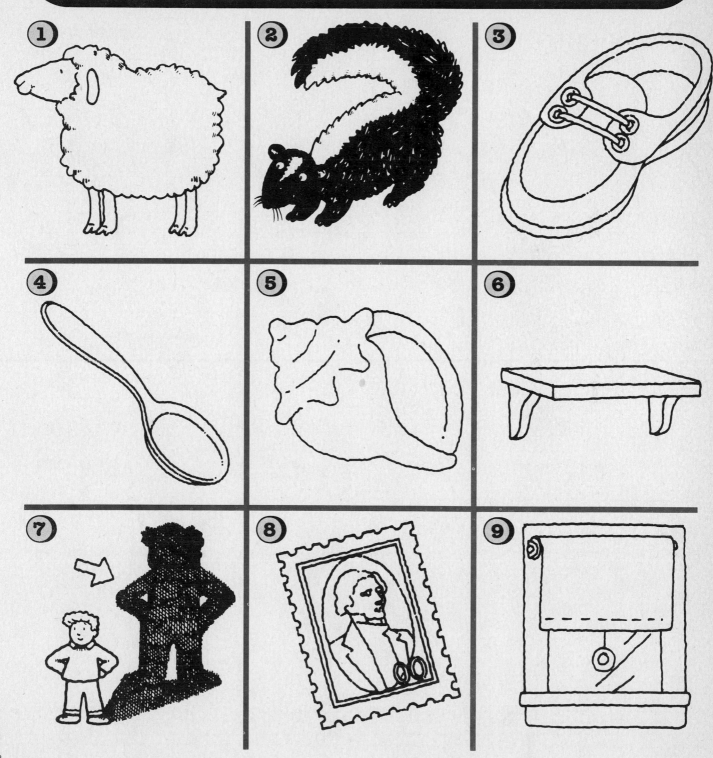

① ② ③
④ ⑤ ⑥
⑦ ⑧ ⑨

LESSON 119: Consonant digraph sh

239

① e ll

② ai l

③ ade

④ ix

⑤ oe

⑥ elf

⑦ ip

⑧ adow

⑨ eat

240 **LESSON 119: Discriminating between sh and s**

Here's what to do!

Chin begins with the sound of **ch**. Color each picture whose name begins with the sound of **ch**.

Here's what to do! Say the name of each picture.
Print **ch** or **c** to finish each word.

① ___ in

② ___ eck

③ ___ oat

④ ___ eese

⑤ ___ ube

⑥ ___ ick

⑦ ___ alk

⑧ ___ ave

⑨ ___ ain

LESSON 120: Discriminating between ch and c

Try this! **Knee** begins with the letters **kn.** You only hear the sound of **n.** Circle the letters that stand for the beginning sound in each word. Color the pictures whose names begin with **kn.**

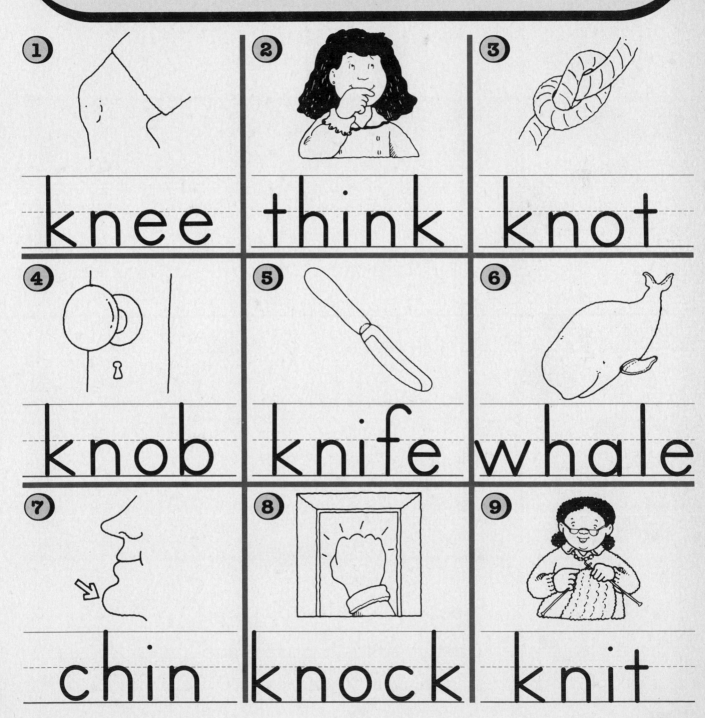

① knee ② think ③ knot

④ knob ⑤ knife ⑥ whale

⑦ chin ⑧ knock ⑨ knit

LESSON 121: Consonant digraph kn

243

1

The tire is black and white.

Chad tied a knot in the rope.

2

Randy did not skin his knee.

Kelly kneels down on the mat.

3

Did you hear a knock at the door?

Did Nick knock over the vase?

4

I fed the bread to the chicks.

I used a knife to slice the cheese.

5

Chuck's watch is on the shelf.

Kate turned the knob to the left.

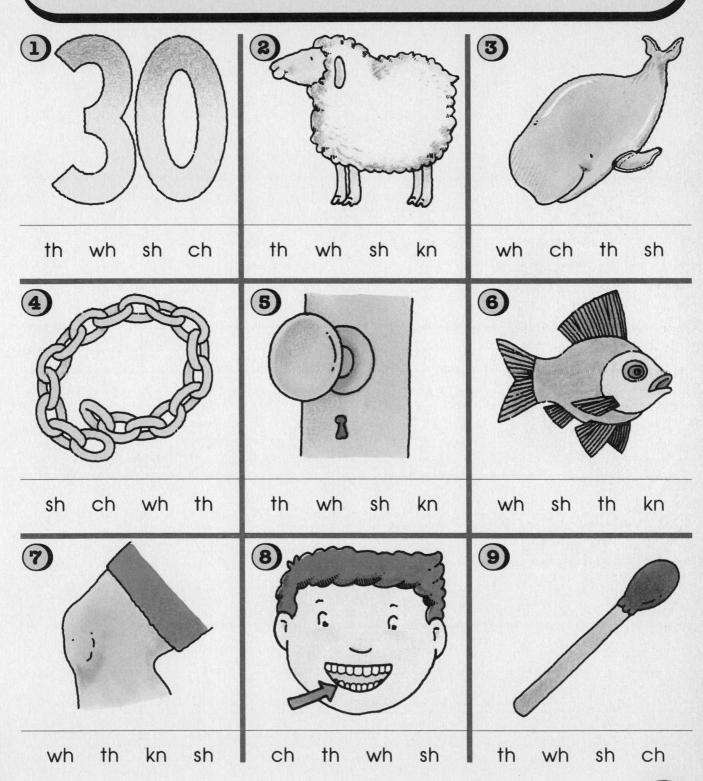

Here's what to do! Say the name of each picture.
Circle the consonant digraph you hear.

1 30
th wh sh ch

2
th wh sh kn

3
wh ch th sh

4
sh ch wh th

5
th wh sh kn

6
wh sh th kn

7
wh th kn sh

8
ch th wh sh

9
th wh sh ch

LESSON 122: Reviewing consonant digraphs

245

1 Do you ___ when we can go to the beach?

know
knob
knock

2 We will catch the bus at ___ .

thick
three
thorn

3 Beth lays a ___ sheet in the shade.

white
wheat
whip

4 We sit and watch the ___ .

shape
ships
shake

5 We fill our shoes with sea ___ !

sheets
shades
shells

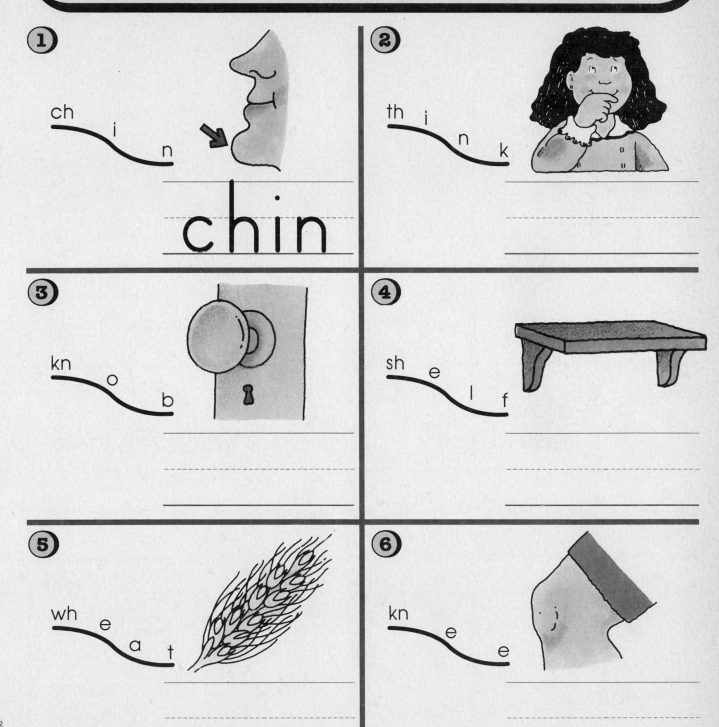

Try this! Say the name of each picture as you slide down the hill. Print it on the line.

1 ch i n

chin

2 th i n k

3 kn o b

4 sh e l f

5 wh e a t

6 kn e e

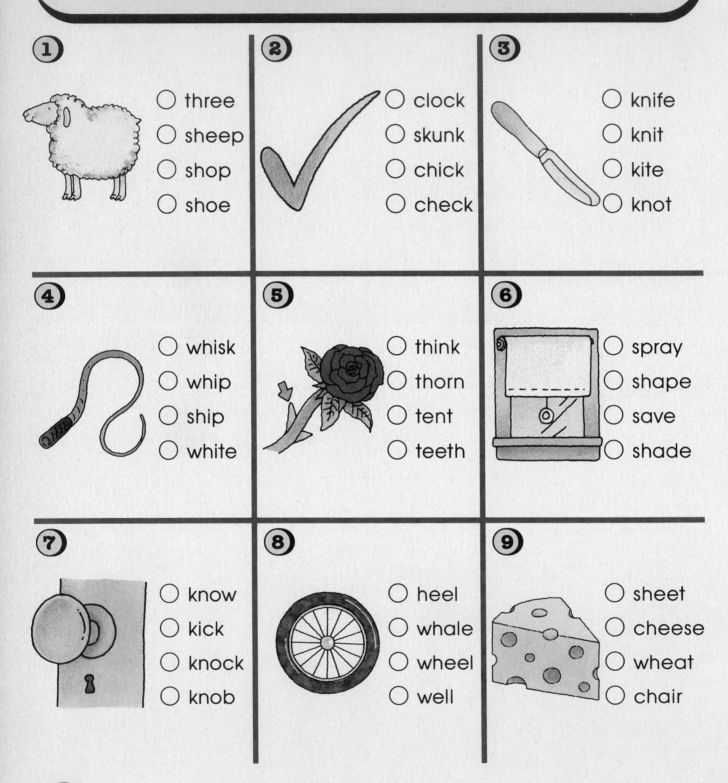

Here's what to do! Fill in the bubble beside the name of each picture.

1
- ○ three
- ○ sheep
- ○ shop
- ○ shoe

2
- ○ clock
- ○ skunk
- ○ chick
- ○ check

3
- ○ knife
- ○ knit
- ○ kite
- ○ knot

4
- ○ whisk
- ○ whip
- ○ ship
- ○ white

5
- ○ think
- ○ thorn
- ○ tent
- ○ teeth

6
- ○ spray
- ○ shape
- ○ save
- ○ shade

7
- ○ know
- ○ kick
- ○ knock
- ○ knob

8
- ○ heel
- ○ whale
- ○ wheel
- ○ well

9
- ○ sheet
- ○ cheese
- ○ wheat
- ○ chair

LESSON 123: Consonant digraph test

Here's what to do! Read the sentence. Circle the short way to say the underlined words.

I will = I'll   you will = you'll
he will = he'll   we will = we'll
she will = she'll   they will = they'll
it will = it'll

1 <u>It will</u> be fun to go for a boat ride.

You'll
It'll
I'll

2 <u>I will</u> get in the boat.

We'll
He'll
I'll

3 <u>You will</u> get in the boat with me.

You'll
She'll
They'll

4 <u>They will</u> all get in the boat, too.

We'll
They'll
It'll

5 Oh no! Get out or <u>we will</u> sink!

he'll
she'll
we'll

 she is = she's

 it is = it's

 he is = he's

1

<u>It is</u> a nice day to play in the park.

_____

_____ a nice day to play in the park.

2

<u>He is</u> going down the slide.

_____

_____ going down the slide.

3

<u>She is</u> floating in the pool.

_____

_____ floating in the pool.

4

<u>It is</u> full of things to do!

_____

_____ full of things to do!

Try this! Look at the picture. Read the sentence.
Print the short way to say the <u>underlined words</u>.

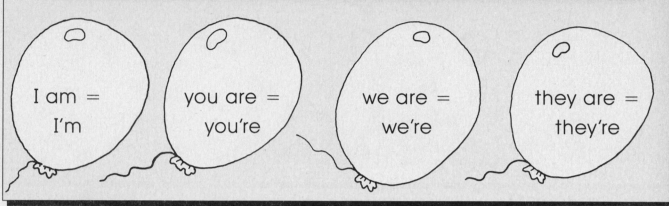

I am =
I'm

you are =
you're

we are =
we're

they are =
they're

1  <u>I am</u> going to the zoo with you and the kids.

_____

_____

_____ going to the zoo with you
and the kids.

2  <u>You are</u> going to see the seals.

_____

_____

_____ going to see the seals.

3 <u>They are</u> going to see the cubs.

_____

_____

_____ going to see the cubs.

4  I think <u>we are</u> going to like the zoo!

_____

_____

I think_____ going to like the zoo!

LESSON 125: Contractions with am and are

251

Here's what to do! Read the sentence. Circle the short way to say the underlined words.

is not = isn't
can not = can't

does not = doesn't
will not = won't

---

1 Wags is a mess!
He <u>is not</u> clean.

can't
doesn't
isn't

---

2 Mom says he needs a bath.
Wags just <u>will not</u> get in the tub.

won't
isn't
doesn't

---

3 Wags <u>does not</u> like baths.
He runs away.

isn't
can't
doesn't

---

4 I <u>can not</u> catch him.
Will you help me?

can't
doesn't
won't

---

5 Wags <u>is not</u> a muddy puppy now.
I am the one who needs a bath!

isn't
can't
doesn't

Here's what to do! Circle the sentence that tells about the picture.

1

I'll eat the hot dog.

I'm going to read the book.

2

It's in the bag.

She'll sleep in the tent.

3

We won't go on the ride.

We're on the ride.

4

She's going to play on the swing.

They're going to like my painting.

5

You're going to rake the yard.

We'll drive up to the lake.

Try this! Fill in the bubble beside the sentence that tells about the picture.

1

○ It's a dog.

○ It can't be a dog.

○ They're dogs.

2

○ He's on a bike.

○ She's in a jet.

○ I'm on the bus.

3

○ It won't rain today.

○ It'll rain all day.

○ I'll play in the rain.

4

○ We don't like bugs.

○ She'll eat a hot dog.

○ We're eating the fruit.

5

○ They'll go for a ride.

○ We'll go for a swim.

○ You're up a tree.

LESSON 126: Reviewing contractions

1 _____ my pet cat.

It's
We're
They'll

2 My cat _____ get down.

he's
can't
she's

3 _____ run and get help.

I'm
I'll
It's

4 _____ get my cat down.

You're
Won't
They'll

5 _____ both very happy now!

We're
She'll
Doesn't

1 _____ going to have a party.

_____
- - - - - - - - - - - -
_____

○ We're
○ We'll
○ Won't

2 _____ tell the kids.

_____
- - - - - - - - - - - -
_____

○ It's
○ She's
○ We'll

3 _____ going to make hats.

_____
- - - - - - - - - - - -
_____

○ You're
○ You'll
○ She'll

4 _____ bring games to play.

_____
- - - - - - - - - - - -
_____

○ Doesn't
○ They'll
○ It'll

5 I _____ wait till the kids come!

_____
- - - - - - - - - - - -
_____

○ isn't
○ can't
○ he's